DIARY
OF A
MALPRACTICE
LAWSUIT

A PHYSICIAN'S JOURNEY AND SURVIVAL GUIDE

BY

JACK SPENSER, M.D.

PREFACE

I'm a physician who got sued for malpractice. This is a diary of that experience. To my knowledge, a work of this kind has never been published. I can think of at least two reasons that this is the case.

First, getting sued is not the high point of anyone's life. I am not going to look particularly good in this book. It was one of the low points of my career, and my life. In this story I am a less sympathetic character than the plaintiff. In fact, my considered opinion is that I may be the least sympathetic character in the book. However, my observation is that in civil lawsuits, it is not necessarily the case that one side is all good and the other side all bad. It's complicated. Also, there is usually not a clear-cut winner or loser. Those getting money via a settlement or verdict wish for more—there was all this suffering for THIS. For the defendant physician, the best that can happen is to be dropped from the lawsuit, or win a jury trial. But this only happens with a successful defense, which takes time, money and effort—months or even years filled with uncertainty and worry. There is no happy ending for anyone.

Second, it takes a lot of energy to write a book, even a bad one. Most lives are filled with career, family, and friends, and there is little time for extra activities. Writing a book is definitely an extra activity. Who needs it? Will anyone read it? Am I wasting my time, and yours?

Why am I writing this book?

I answer with the reasons I read, which are numerous. I read to be entertained, and I hope to make this book interesting enough to be entertaining. I read to learn, and I will relate facts and experiences not generally known.

However, the main reason I read is to know that I AM NOT ALONE. My insecurities, vulnerabilities, and challenges are shared by other humans. We all mess up, recover, and regroup, and live to make more mistakes. I am hanging in there by my fingernails, same as everybody else.

When you are sued, you are alone. A lawsuit is an intersection of patient and physician where your mistakes and vulnerabilities are exposed. A malpractice lawsuit shines a spotlight on your life, at least your professional life, looking at everything to see if there was a mistake, negligence. That has been my experience. Did I screw up? Did I do enough? What could I have done differently? Am I a good person?

Who should read this book?

Physicians should read this book.

Ask any physician, "What has been the worst experience of your *professional* life?" and almost invariably the answer is, "Getting sued for malpractice." A lot of doctors have this worst experience. One in fourteen physicians gets sued every year. Almost every physician will face a malpractice suit, or more than one, during his or her career. That certainly tracks with my experience. Almost every doctor I know has been sued at least once. This written record will tell you that you are not alone.

Patients should read this book.

A lawsuit involves conflict, and life is full of conflict, so this book should resonate with even non-physician readers. A patient might also wish to see a malpractice lawsuit from the perspective of the physician, a side of the story not usually told, if ever. In popular media—TV, film, books—the viewpoint of the patient/plaintiff is always sympathetically expressed, but not the physician, who is usually portrayed as a greedy doctor. A good example is *The Verdict*, an excellent film in which Paul Newman plays a heroic plaintiff's attorney, and the other side is portrayed as a bunch of greedy lying physicians and executive bullies. That is a good story, worth telling, but has been told many times. Even if that were my experience, I could not tell that story better than it has already been told. I want to tell a different story, so I don't have to compete with other writers, who are probably better than me. What I can do is something different: tell the story of a lawsuit from the view of a defendant physician and physician-owned company.

I can tell the truth.

CHAPTER 1

Tuesday, February 18, Year 1

The lawsuit grabbed me this afternoon. Someone from the sheriff's office brought it to our business office. "I'm just the messenger," he told our business manager, Janet. I was working at one of our hospitals, not the business office, so Janet phoned me with the calamitous news.

I'm scared. Like most physicians, I am an obedient person who follows the rules. That's how I became a physician. Renegade rebels do not become physicians, but go into more lucrative, interesting careers like motorcycle gang leaders. Becoming a physician is the result of winning lots of competitions. Relatively few who apply to medical school get in, and I needed to study hard and get good grades to be considered, and get a good score on the Medical College Admissions Test (MCAT). I had to obey the rules, too. Once in medical school, it's a good idea to do what you are told, and learn. There are countless tests to take. I had to pass three national board tests to be eligible for a medical license.

After medical school comes residency. My memory of residency is being in a pack of wolves, all trying to keep up and do an impossible job, with long hours and incredible fatigue. Like a wolf pack, the members would turn and tear to pieces anyone who could not keep up. Not everyone made it through the four-year residency. *St. Elsewhere* is the only TV program that has come close to telling what academic medicine is really like, with the fatigue (holding a retractor during surgery, fighting sleep), and the sudden changes (a dull emergency room, everyone sitting around drinking coffee, and then everything crashes). The last step in training was to pass the Boards in Anatomic and Clinical Pathology. That was a three-day examination.

After the training came the applications to get a state license and to be on a hospital medical staff. Any black mark on your record can disqualify you. Society gives great responsibility and rewards to physicians. Physicians have great power, literally life and death. This power is not given lightly or cavalierly. One had better have good recommendations from teachers and colleagues. There had better not be anything troubling in your record, like an arrest or drug use. Your record should demonstrate that you play well with others. Nonconformists are shunned.

The end result is that I, like most physicians, obey the rules—I get frightened when I see OTHER cars stopped for speeding.

When Janet phoned me about the lawsuit, I was in an office in one of our three hospital laboratories, where I spend most of my time. There I sit in a chair without armrests, looking at glass slides through my gray binocular AO 110 microscope, dictating microscopic descriptions, comments, and diagnoses with hands-free dictating equipment, moving slides across the stage of my microscope, and I am most alive, at my best, doing what I am supposed to do, that very few can do. I am a physician/pathologist—a scientist, one who studies disease. If a patient has a lesion, I am the one who figures out what it is, and makes a diagnosis. Dermatologists send me skin biopsies, and I diagnose the cause of the rash or lesion. A surgeon will send me an appendix, and I will tell him whether or not it has acute appendicitis—whether that was the cause of the patient's abdominal pain. Urologists send prostate tissue to me, to determine whether it is benign or malignant. A chest surgeon can send me a portion of a lung with cancer, with lymph nodes, and my job is to discern the type of lung cancer and the extent of the spread of the tumor. Doctors and patients send me tissue specimens to examine, to see what's going on. Like you may have done in high school or college biology class, with a frog or a shark, I try to identify structures and lesions. I sample the specimens, and from those tissues, microscopic tissue slides are made and stained. I look at those slides and make the final diagnoses—benign, malignant, infectious, inflammatory, normal…

It's all I ever wanted to do. When I was about five years old or so, the term "pathologist" came up in a conversation—What's a pathologist? I asked. The answer was a person who examines a dead person and tries to figure out why he died. Everyone was grossed out except me. I thought it sounded kinda neat, to scientifically examine a body to figure out what happened. As I got older, my interest in science continued. I was one of those kids who had a chemistry set you could buy out of a catalog, and I would make hydrogen sulfide, stink up the house, and try to make a bomb. Luckily I survived. When I was nine, some friends and I put dry ice into a bottle of water, watched everything bubble up, and closed the lid to see what would happen. Eventually my dad saw what was happening and took the lid off before the bottle exploded. I was a rock hound with a collection of obsidian, granite, mica, and shale. I caught caterpillars, put them in a bottle, and watched them become cocoons and butterflies. It was natural that when I grew up, I became a scientist, and hopefully a healer as well.

I'm in private practice, a suburban/rural practice, in Dallas, Texas. There are five pathologists in our group, covering three small- to medium-sized hospitals (Pinnacle, Suburban, and Rural), a few surgery centers, and a number of doctor's offices. Anatomic pathology is what we do.

Each day I go to work at one of the three hospitals, and on many days I'm by myself. Therefore, to consult with colleagues about various matters, including this lawsuit, I have to use the telephone. Therefore much of this book describes phone calls made and received in one of our three hospital offices, which are pretty much the same. Each is Spartan with a desk, microscope, chair, and desktop computer to use to access patients' medical records, dictating equipment, and bookshelves with medical texts. That's pretty much it. There is a door opening to the laboratory. There are no windows. Outside my office, the laboratory provides background noise with centrifuges humming, instruments swishing, telephones ringing, and technologists talking.

Janet drove over and handed the lawsuit to me. She is a thin anxious person, with reddish brown hair, who looks as if at any minute life will overwhelm her. She had obviously been crying.

I started to read it, and I wanted to cry too. I was too busy to read the whole thing. Nobody called time-out from the rest of my duties so I could read it in an uninterrupted fashion.

I went home and read the lawsuit after dinner. It's seven legal-sized pages long, actually relatively brief.

The plaintiff is Lynn Hawthorne. She is thirty-six years old.

I'm one of the defendants. My fellow defendants are my partners Larry Roundtree, M.D., and Reynolds Price, M.D. Pathology Services, P.C., an anatomic pathology company we own, is also named in the lawsuit. Finally, John Pelton, M.D., a physician/pathologist employee, is named.

The complaint is relatively simple and pertains to "collected cervical specimen tissue (Pap smears) for evaluation and diagnosis… On the following dates: August 12… and September 14 [Note, a little over a year later]… The defendants were negligent in their examination, identification, and classification in that they failed to identify and report abnormal cells which were present."

In simple terms, we blew it.

It gets worse.

Further, the complaint alleges "As a result of the negligence of the defendants, by the time the cervical cancer was properly diagnosed, Ms. Hawthorne was required to undergo a radical abdominal hysterectomy and lymph node removal on March 15…" That is to say six months after the Pap smears, she had to have her uterus, tubes, and ovaries removed, as well as part of her vagina and nearby lymph nodes.

It gets worse.

"She was required to undergo another surgery on August 13, six months after the first surgery, to remove additional malignancy in her pelvis." The cancer came back.

It gets worse.

"Ms. Hawthorne is currently undergoing radiation therapy. Her life expectancy is adversely affected by the negligent delay in rendering a correct diagnosis."

It can't get any worse. That her life is "adversely affected" is a tremendous understatement. She does not have long to live.

On to the DAMAGES part, which reads "The quality of her life has been altered and she has suffered a great deal of pain and suffering and mental anguish. Lynn Hawthorne continues to receive medical care and treatment for her cancer. Her life expectancy is adversely affected." For this, "the plaintiff Lynn Hawthorne demands of the defendants the sum of TEN MILLION AND NO/100 DOLLARS ($10,000,000.00) as compensation."

What an arena I am in. Let's take a hard look at the case, from what little information is available. I know the jury will side with the plaintiff. We can be faultless, and we will probably lose. I am a prosperous physician, in my late forties, in good health, married, with a nice home and family, with a reasonable expectation of a long and happy life. The jury will have no sympathy for me. The plaintiff is a single mom with limited financial resources but a good work ethic, who is going to die a painful death in the not too distant future. The jury will have a lot of sympathy for her. My legal judgment, for what it's worth, is that we will have to settle, or lose a jury verdict.

Of course I whine; I don't think it's fair. Everyone makes mistakes, including me. We are all human, including physicians, including this physician. There is no class or training in medical school or in residency about how to handle mistakes. The unstated assumption is that an excellent physician does not make mistakes. This is preposterous. No one can be perfect. Practice does not make perfect. Practice makes better.

What's a reasonable error rate? And don't say zero, because that is not possible. Even Jesus only got eleven out of twelve right, and no physician/pathologist is Jesus. Also, what I do is not particularly straightforward. Discerning benign tissue from malignant tissue is not easy, and there are countless disease conditions to consider with each slide, and the stakes are enormous. The cells under the microscope do not line up to spell BENIGN or MALIGNANT, or whatever the lesion is.

That's enough statistics. Let's humanize this. I hope I always remember that important persons are waiting for my "verdict"—physicians, patients, family members and friends. Pretty much every diagnosis I make is life changing. That is obvious if the diagnosis is something like breast or prostate cancer, which leads to dramatic treatment options. Figuring out the cause of an infection can lead to a cure. Less dramatically, a diagnosis of benign leads to peace of mind, also life changing in a way.

I have to do the job pretty much no matter the circumstances. We run pretty lean; there is no backup except under emergency conditions. So if I have been throwing up all night or my back hurts or my neck hurts—I still have to work and concentrate. If I am quarrelling with someone—my neighbor, a colleague, a family member, whoever—I still have to work and concentrate. I know all jobs can be like that to some extent, but what I am trying to convey is that there is no way to have a bad day. The specimens just keep coming.

Of course, it's not always that challenging and difficult. Many decisions are not life and death, and the vast majority of decisions I make are obvious and do not take much time or energy. Even if I miss something, there are second chances—procedures can be repeated, a follow-up specimen can be collected, and there are quality-control measures in place that can correct a mistake before it is too late.

I can think of about three meaningful mistakes I have made. There was a thyroid gland, and I diagnosed it as Hashimoto's thyroiditis, an inflammatory condition; it was actually a malignant lymphoma—about four months after my misdiagnosis, it metastasized to the abdomen. I misdiagnosed a cytology specimen from the kidney system as malignant; when the kidney was removed, the changes in the kidney were inflammatory and benign. Finally, in a stomach specimen I diagnosed a benign peptic ulcer, which was actually linitiis plastica, a highly malignant stomach cancer, which eventually killed the patient. This mistake is amazingly easy to make; there is a sick joke among pathologists that goes like this: there are two kinds of pathologists in the world—those who have missed linitiis plastica and those who will miss linitiis plastica.

That's about it. The crazy thing is that I did not get sued for any of these cases. Oh, I've been sued all right, several times. But never for a mistake. Usually I have been sued because the health system failed the patient in some way, and I was blamed. One lawsuit went to trial, and I won the jury trial. The rest of the cases were dropped, because there was nothing there. I did nothing wrong, and the plaintiffs and their lawyers decided to stop wasting their time and money. I find that amazing, that when I messed up, nothing happened, but the few times I have been sued, I did everything right. Also, unlike in the present case, the plaintiffs were not sympathetic and did much themselves to bring on their problems. The juries would not have been sympathetic to the plaintiffs.

But there is more to the story than simply relating that I did not get sued when I made mistakes, bad mistakes. How do I live with myself? How do other physicians who make comparable mistakes (and believe me they do) live with themselves? Well, everyone has to kill their own snakes.

I don't know what others do, and as I said earlier, I am not aware of any training or coursework that any physician receives to address this issue.

Here is what I do. I recognize that I am human. I take pride in my work, and I get enough positive reinforcement from colleagues and patients to think I do a good job, so when I do make a mistake, I can live with it, recognizing those are the consequences of playing in the arena I play in. Knowing that what I do is important keeps me motivated and makes me think I make a difference in the world. It is my contribution. When I make a mistake, I admit it as soon as possible (no sense in hiding it) and try to move forward with what can be done NOW.

Anyone considering going into medicine needs to think about how to cope with mistakes. Consider whether you can live with the consequences of a mistake that can be enormous, literally life and death. If you don't think you can handle it and live with yourself, consider another calling.

So, in this case, did I make a mistake? I don't know. First I have to do some more exposition. This lawsuit involves Pap smears, and in most labs most Pap smears are not examined by pathologists, they are examined by cytotechnologists. Pathologists review all ABNORMAL Pap smears and 10% of the normal ones for quality control. Maybe I never saw the slides in question. Maybe the mistake, if there was a mistake, was not done by me.

We are being sued because today a death from cervical cancer is rare and regarded as an outlier, a mistake. Previous generations would be astonished at this turn of events. At the beginning of the twentieth century, cancer of the cervix was a common disease and the most frequent fatal cancer in women, in large part because it was usually not detected until it was at an advanced incurable stage.

From the early 1900s to the present there have been the following trends:

1. A marked decrease in cervical cancer in the advanced stage that Ms. Hawthorne has.

2. A resultant decrease in mortality.

3. A corresponding increase in the detection of early cervical lesions that are precursors to advanced stages, and these early lesions can be treated and cured.

The person most responsible for this success story is George Papanicolaou (1883–1962), who discovered the Pap smear named after him. Dr. Papanicolaou was able to observe that there were differences in the appearance of cells from a normal cervix and a malignant cervix and that these differences could be discerned by taking smears from the vagina, staining them, and looking at them under the microscope. This simple test detected cancers before they were clinically apparent by signs and symptoms.

Over time it was discovered that cervical cancer, like most cancers, is often (always?) preceded by cellular abnormalities called dysplasia, or early noninvasive cancer (carcinoma in situ). The theory then is that invasive non-curable cervical cancer is the end result of a process that starts as mild dysplasia, goes to moderate dysplasia, severe dysplasia, carcinoma in situ, ending in invasive carcinoma. The trick of the thing, then, is to detect early lesions, which can be treated and obliterated before invasive carcinoma develops, which can be difficult to impossible to cure.

The more I study cancer, the more I think this is the model for most cancer—a precursor lesion, then carcinoma in situ, and finally an invasive tumor. As discovered by Dr. Papanicolaou, this insight was first apparent with cervical cancer, but to me it appears to hold true for other organs as well, e.g., breast, lung, prostate, urinary bladder, perhaps all organs.

The widespread use of Pap smears has allowed the diagnosis of these early lesions of dysplasia and carcinoma in situ before the development of invasive carcinomas, and treatment of these early lesions has largely contributed to the decreasing death rate from cervical cancer to the present. Specifically, cervical cancer deaths have decreased by 74% in the last fifty years.

In the future there will be even less cervical cancer. The cause of almost all cervical cancers is the human papillomavirus (HPV). The HPV vaccines against various strains of HPV reduce the risk of precancerous or cancerous changes in the cervix by about 93%, so invasive cervical cancer can't develop. The hope is that cervical cancer will go the way of polio eventually and be eliminated.

Unfortunately all this is too late for Lynn Hawthorne. She is way past the stage where vaccination or anything else will do any good.

CHAPTER 2

Wednesday, February 19, Year 1

I was working at Suburban Hospital today, and first thing this morning I phoned the folks at my malpractice insurance carrier, Mutual Malpractice, and gave them the bad news. This was a cover-my-rear-end call. Dr. Reynolds Price, one of my partners, had already phoned them yesterday, so they know about the lawsuit. I just want them to know I am being sued as well and need some help. I talked to Milton Jackson, one of the Mutual Malpractice staff attorneys. His job is not to defend us, but he will assign an attorney in private practice to do that, and pay the fees. "Who all was named in the suit?" Mr. Jackson asked.

I read the list to him.

Mr. Jackson said, "Since none of the pathologists saw the slides, I think you should be dropped from the suit."

"I totally agree with that. I don't know the legal details, but I would prefer the company be named as a defendant corporation, rather than each of us as individuals."

"I don't think the plaintiff's attorney will agree," he said. "Dr. Price has asked for a good attorney to defend you—Lowell Pound. I think we can get him."

"That's good."

"Mutual Malpractice will defend you."

"Thanks," I said. "Anything more I need to do at present?"

"No. Dr. Price is going to send over a copy of the lawsuit."

"I received the lawsuit yesterday at 3 p.m., so we haven't had a chance to gather up much information—quality control data and so forth. I hope to have that info this afternoon, and then I can tell you more."

"Good."

A very unpleasant conversation. No one likes to talk about screw-ups. I do hope Milton Jackson is right in his belief that none of the pathologists saw the Pap smears. At this point, I really don't know if that is the case. It makes a big difference to me. I do not feel as culpable if I didn't see the slides. I must say, though, that if I didn't see the slides, I need to look hard at what I am doing for a living. Assuming I did not see the slides, I am being sued for $10 million by a woman I never met, about slides I never saw. I dislike the liability for things I can control, but this is liability I cannot control. I feel helpless. This is the life of a healer?

On the way home from the hospital, I stopped at our business office/laboratory so I could check with Carolyn Herring, our cytology prep person. She does much of the prep work and paperwork regarding Pap smears. She is big and no-nonsense, with a handgun-carry permit and a revolver in her purse.

I told her what had happened, which I am sure she already knew. I established what we were going to do, which is fairly simple at this point. One file cabinet drawer will hold all the documents related to the lawsuit. Under no circumstances is the original paperwork to leave the premises, only copies.

"Did any of the pathologists look at the Pap smears?" I asked.

"No."

Thank God.

Thursday, February 20, Year 1

For the first time I talked to Dr. Larry Roundtree, my other partner, about the lawsuit. He is quite angry at our local academic institution, Ivory Hospital, particularly at Dr. Helen Smith, a gynecologist on staff there, part of the ob-gyn faculty. She was a professor of mine back when I was a medical student. I think she is an okay physician, not a bad teacher, not a good one. At this point in her career she is an ob-gyn oncologist, who specializes in patients like Lynn Hawthorne. I am not sure how good Dr. Smith is at that either. She sure didn't help a friend of mine much when she had cervical cancer. She died. I knew her when she was a nursing student at the same time I was a medical student; she eventually married a pediatrician, who is also a friend of mine. Under the rather ineffective care of Dr. Smith, my friend died a horrible death from cervical cancer, in pain and losing weight to the point she looked like a concentration camp victim. The last time I saw my friend was in a hallway at Pinnacle Hospital. We talked. It was a poignant conversation because we both knew it would be our last conversation.

She said, "Looking back at my life, I put up with too much bullshit. I'm tired of it. Life is too short for that."

I was not involved in her care at all, nor was our lab, but there was a rumor of some malpractice in her care—something to the effect that there was an abnormal Pap smear, and there was a failure to communicate this to the patient, so that there was no follow-up, so the cancer grew until it was too late for a cure, and then a cover-up, even to the point of changing the medical record. I repeat, I was not involved in my friend's care at all, so I do not know any of this as a fact, only what I heard. At any rate, losing a nurse, the wife of a physician, to cervical cancer is a bad look.

I do know for a fact what Dr. Smith has done to us. She borrowed the Pap smears from us—ostensibly to review them as part of the care of Lynn Hawthorne when she was referred to her for treatment. By the time Dr. Smith saw the patient, she already had cervical cancer, which was obvious by simply doing a physical exam, and her cancer had already been confirmed by a tissue biopsy. What the Pap smear showed at that point had absolutely no bearing on her care. As a courtesy, we sent the Pap smears to Dr. Smith, as we do for any request from another physician or hospital. Dr. Smith never returned OUR Pap smears to us. She sent them to the law firm of Lichty and Francis, who sued us. Dr. Smith didn't want the Pap smears to help with Ms. Hawthorne's care. She wanted the Pap smears to help with Ms. Hawthorne's lawsuit. In decades of practice, this is the most backstabbing attack that has ever happened to me.

"It's unethical," said my partner. "I don't want to make a federal case out of this, because we may need Ivory Hospital's help to defend this thing."

"Ivory will not help us defend this case," I said. "No one will help us."

"I know. Everyone will say this didn't happen on my watch."

Later, I talked by phone to Dr. John Pelton, one of our employee pathologists. He is very angry about being named in the lawsuit. I don't blame him. He was probably named because his name is on the letterhead of the Pap smear report, no other reason. He is not an owner of the company, he didn't look at the Pap smears, and he had nothing to do with the specimens. John validly complained, "They might as well have named one of our secretaries or couriers…"

"They probably will," I replied.

He was not amused.

Feelings today: I am getting ready for a long struggle, although my guess is that this case will be settled long before a trial.

CHAPTER 3

Friday, February 21, Year 1

It's been a long week. I must have looked depressed when I woke up. "I'm here for you," said Sarah, my wife.

"That won't make the lawsuit go away," I said.

"Want to talk about it?"

"That won't make the lawsuit go away."

"But it can help to talk about it."

"That won't make the lawsuit go away."

I went to work. Here is how my day goes. I stop by our laboratory on the way to the hospital and pick up microscopic slides, which are bundled with the typed-up gross descriptions of the specimens. Gross descriptions are the documented observations that the pathologist dictates as he examines the specimen—size of the specimen, location of any lesion, size of lesion The gross description usually includes what parts of the specimen are submitted for microscopic examination, and how the resultant microscopic slides will be labelled.

I finish the drive to my office at one of our three hospitals. I spend much of the morning looking through the microscope at sections of essentially every organ in the body: skin, breast, stomach, colon, brain, appendix, gallbladder… the list is endless. I look at what is there and dictate a microscopic description and diagnosis for each specimen.

When I am done with microscopic exams, I go to the gross room, where I examine the specimens from the day: colons, gastrointestinal biopsies, breasts, skin tissue, gallbladders, appendices, brain biopsies… an endless variety. I dissect and describe the specimens, taking samples as I go, putting them in tissue cassettes, which go into formaldehyde. I also dictate my findings using hands-free dictating equipment. The cassettes are collected at the end of the day by our couriers, processed overnight at our business office/lab, and from the resultant paraffin blocks, microscopic slides are prepared. I pick them up in the morning, or the courier brings them to me at the hospital, and the process repeats. I wear light blue scrubs.

I am always interested to look at the slides and see what's there. I am interrupted by operating room consults, usually involving frozen sections. A frozen section means I freeze a sample of the specimen—breast tissue, lymph node, whatever—cut a microscopic section, stain the tissue on the slide, look at it through the microscope, and render a diagnosis, a preliminary diagnosis. All this takes about twenty minutes. The final diagnosis happens the next day when I look at the additional permanent sections, which are made after overnight processing.

There are other interruptions: sometimes I do bone marrow exams. This involves drawing bone marrow out of bone from the iliac crest or sternum. This is my only direct patient contact. There are interruptions from the laboratory staff from the hematology, blood bank, chemistry, and microbiology sections.

Last but not least, Pap smears are an important part of the operation. Clinicians, often ob-gyn specialists, collect the specimens, basically swabs from the cervix/vagina, and smear them on slides. Those slides are placed in a fixative and stained with the Papanicolaou stain. They are looked at (screened) by a cytotechnologist, who marks the abnormal cells, usually with an ink circle. I look at the abnormal Pap smears, which will have the abnormal cells circled, and confirm or change the interpretations of the cytotechnologists. Also, I look at 10% of the normal unmarked Pap smears as a quality control measure. This is the way we do Pap smears, which is the way labs throughout the country do Pap smears.

It's a high-stakes high-stress environment. The field of pathology attracts adrenaline junkies. In their free time, they tend to be scuba divers (I'm one) or mountain climbers, like Beck Weathers, a pathologist who was part of the ill-fated Mount Everest expedition described by Jon Krakauer in *Into Thin Air*, or do other risky things—fly airplanes, drive motorcycles—live on the edge.

CHAPTER 4

Friday, March 7, Year 1

Today I was working in my office at Pinnacle Hospital, the busiest of our three hospitals. Nevertheless I had some free time, so I phoned Bruce Palmore, the cytotechnologist who looked at one of the slides. He works for us part time. His full-time job is at Carswell Air Force Base in nearby Fort Worth. To earn extra money, he works as a cytotechnologist for us, mainly on weekends. We pay him on a per slide basis; he keeps track of the slides he screens, and we pay him a fee per slide. He is an outstanding cytotechnologist. The Air Force is lucky to have him, and so are we. He had screened one of the Pap smears involved in the lawsuit. I was afraid no one had told him about the lawsuit, a lawsuit he is now a part of. I was right. Bruce didn't know a thing about it. I don't remember much about the conversation, but he was upset about the bad news.

After this awkward conversation, I pulled out my file on the lawsuit and came across a letter from Lowell Pound, our lawyer. One of his commandments is not to talk to ANYONE about the case.

What the hell does that mean? Lowell cannot mean not to talk to literally anyone about the case. That is impossible. I just got off the phone talking to Bruce Palmore about the case, because somebody has to let him know what is going on. This is an example of the ambiguities and inconsistencies of a lawsuit, which are maddening to me, a scientist who is used to dealing with concrete facts.

So let's break it down. Does that mean I can't discuss the case with other doctors? Yeah, it probably does. That means I cannot get any support from my colleagues.

Does that mean I can't talk to my friends about the case? Yeah, it probably does. That means no support from my friends.

Does that mean I can't talk to my wife and kids about the case? Yeah, it probably does. A total blackout, though, is not really practical. For logistical reasons, I am going to have to tell my family something: an obvious example is when I go to give a deposition, I need to tell my family where I am going, and why I am not going to the hospital.

Nevertheless, the imperative of Lowell is not to talk to anyone about the case.

I am alone.

I am thinking about quitting and retiring from medicine. This lawsuit may be the last straw. Why?

Pretty much every day I hear complaints about turnaround times for complete blood counts, frozen sections, special stains, routine stains… pretty much everything I do. Nothing is ever done quickly enough for our customers—clinicians and their patients. "I just want an answer" is the refrain, and God help me if I'm wrong.

I endure a lot of inspections. Our laboratory is inspected by the state, the Joint Commission on Accreditation of Hospitals, and the College of American Pathologists. I do not have a particularly high regard for the inspectors. I have to listen to criticism of our laboratory from someone I don't think has enough talent to work FOR me, let alone tell me how to do things.

The biggest reason I want to quit, though, is the threat of malpractice suits. Pathologists are like accountants. We look at tissues and do lab work for almost every patient who comes in to the hospital—and for virtually all the physicians on the medical staff, the good and the bad. When a business deal goes south, the accountants have to testify and maybe even are named as defendants. Enron went out of business, but so did their accountants, Arthur Anderson. So it is when medical care goes awry, and the lawsuits come, the pathologist ends up in the middle and gets dragged into the lawsuit, as an expert witness or even a defendant. This is not my first lawsuit, and unless I quit, it won't be the last.

I'm really tired.

But not too tired to type up a letter of resignation. Just as I finished, Reynolds Price called. "How's it going?" he asked.

"I'm resigning."

He laughed. "You must be having a really bad day."

"No, I'm really quitting." I read him my letter of resignation.

"I think you're making a mistake," he said. "The case may be settled. Once everything is laid out, it may be settled. It's stressful, but basically it will come out all right. You're better off working than sitting at home stewing over it."

"I'll tear up my resignation." And I did.

I told Sarah what happened when I got home. "I don't think you will be working there much longer," she said.

I am seriously thinking about leaving medicine to pursue a career as a writer. I think I have some writing talent. Earlier this year *Leisure Magazine* published a travel piece I wrote about Cape Cod whales, and paid me $450, so I am already a published writer. I have written a few dozen short stories, and about one of them, the fiction editor at *The New Yorker* said I "write awfully well" although he passed on the piece. I have written two screenplays, which are on file at Warner Brothers and MGM studios. Of course, every taxicab driver in Los Angeles has two screenplays on file at Warner Brothers and MGM studios and probably every other studio.

Tim Anderson, a local poet, has been a mentor to me. Every Sunday afternoon we meet at Shoney's and go over my writing and talk. "I'm sure you have a lot to contribute in medicine," he has said, "but I think you have a lot to contribute in writing. When you hit, everyone in the world will want to take credit for your success. Just remember who believed in you from the start."

CHAPTER 5

Thursday, March 20, Year 1

Reynolds phoned me at home today, on my day off, to tell me Lowell needs a bunch of documents:

1. The error rate for Bruce Palmore, the cytotechnologist who examined one of the Pap smears.

2. The error rate for Billy Swenson, the cytotechnologist who examined the other Pap smear.

3. Finally, Lowell wants to know: Where is Billy Swenson?

Good question. He doesn't work for us anymore. When he did work for us, he was only part time, same as Bruce Palmore, and same as Bruce, he was in the Air Force stationed at nearby Carswell Air Force Base. The two of them worked nights and weekends, because we were unsuccessful in recruiting a full-time staff cytotechnologist. It was that suboptimal arrangement or discontinue doing Pap smears. In retrospect, I wish we had stopped doing Pap smears. Then we wouldn't be in this mess. Anyway, our Pap smear volume went down, and we didn't need both cytotechnologists. Our opinion was that Bruce was the better screener, so we kept Bruce and let Billy go. I suspect he is still in the Air Force, but I don't know that for sure. I think we have his address and phone number on file.

According to Reynolds, the plaintiff's attorneys still have the Pap smears and are still getting experts to review them. I have been photocopying like crazy, article after article about Pap smears, and sending the information to Lowell Pound, our defense attorney.

"He won't read all that," said Reynolds.

"I think he will," I replied.

"Dr. Ted Gable at the University of Arkansas Medical Center is someone who may be willing to be an expert witness for us."

"I've heard him give presentations at some national meetings. He's good."

So the plaintiffs are getting medical experts to review the slides. I have no doubt those experts will say we messed up, because of retrospective bias, a phenomenon well known to me. What's retrospective bias?

Say there are two ways to drive to downtown Dallas from our lab, one by interstate highway and the other using secondary roads. You make a decision—interstate, and get caught behind a horrible accident that blocks all lanes, and you sit for hours. You made the wrong decision, retrospective bias. Turn it around, and take secondary roads, and run into unexpected road construction—you made a wrong decision, and had you the chance to do it over again, you would have taken the interstate—retrospective bias.

Let's bring it to medicine. A patient has a bleeding peptic ulcer of the stomach. Two choices, operate or treat medically. Let's say the decision is made to operate—remove the ulcer, stop the bleeding, and save a life. But the patient dies of complications from the operation. In retrospect, it would have been better to treat medically—retrospective bias. Okay, but let's go back in time and treat the bleeding peptic ulcer medically, but the patient's bleeding gets worse, and the patient bleeds to death. Retrospective bias—it would have been better to operate.

Let's bring it to pathology. If a Pap smear is interpreted as negative, as we did with Lynn Hawthorne's specimen, and the patient goes on to die of cervical cancer, retrospective bias comes in, and the interpretation is that we messed up and committed malpractice. But let's turn it around. Suppose we diagnosed the Pap smear as malignant, and when the follow-up specimens (biopsies, resection…) were benign, again the retrospective bias interpretation would be we messed up and committed malpractice.

Well, Jack, you say, why don't you just get it right and you wouldn't have this problem?

And I reply, "It's impossible to always 'get it right.'" In each Pap smear there are 200,000 to 300,000 cells, and *in retrospect,* it is always possible to find abnormal cells—retrospective bias.

It is the bane of a pathologist's existence. The slides we look at last forever. Anyone can look at them months or years later, with additional clinical information, results of follow-up studies, additional X-rays, follow-up tissue like the resection specimen—and come up with a more informed diagnosis and second-guess the pathologist making the original diagnosis on the tissue specimen based on the clinical information available at the time—retrospective bias.

So, in the present set of circumstances, here is what is going to happen: The Pap smears will go to the plaintiff's medical experts, who will look at the 200,000 to 300,000 cells on the slide, find a few funny-looking cells (which are present in every Pap smear), take a photomicrograph of the cells under high magnification, magnify *that* image, project it on a screen with a normal cell next to it, and present that to the jury, saying, "See, it is impossible to miss such an abnormality." Not fair, not fair at all, but that is what will happen if this case goes to trial.

Thursday, March 26, Year 1

We've located Billy Swenson, who is still in the Air Force at Fort Worth.

Also, we finally got possession of Lynn Hawthorne's Pap smears today. I examined them, and unfortunately, neither one of the Pap smears in my opinion is negative (normal):

The earlier Pap smear has some mildly abnormal cells and some changes of HPV (human papillomavirus). There are also some trichomonas organisms, little organisms that can cause inflammation of the cervix and vagina. The Pap smear is also loaded with blood.

The later Pap smear has some mildly abnormal cells and changes of HPV.

Tough to know where this leaves us. Retrospective bias applies to me as well. I have never seen the slides until now, and I have no idea what diagnoses I would have given these specimens if I didn't already know the outcome—that she has incurable cervical cancer.

Friday, March 27, Year 1

Reynolds Price, my partner, looked at the Pap smears and phoned me with his impressions. He is board certified not only in anatomic and clinical pathology (as am I) but also cytopathology, so I am interested in his diagnoses. He thinks the first Pap smear is normal. The second slide, in his opinion, shows a high-grade lesion, in other words, something bad.

There is some good news, though. Lowell Pound, our attorney, thinks he may be able to get us dropped from the lawsuit as individuals. That has been my thinking all along, since we never looked at the Pap smears. I know that we will still be responsible as owners of the laboratory where all this happened, but I want to be dropped as an individual. Lowell's thinking is this: Dr. Mary Bishop, the patient's gynecologist, collected the Pap smears. She sent the slides to Pathology Services, P.C., to interpret them. Pathology Services paid two cytotechnologists, Bruce Palmore and Billy Swenson, to interpret the Pap smears. Why should we, the pathologists, be the only ones sued? In fact, why should we be sued at all? So goes Lowell's thinking. I'm not sure this is a winning argument. My first rule of lawsuits is that no one knows anything.

Friday, April 4, Year 1

We are finally fighting back. Lowell Pound sent over the answers we will give to the allegations in the lawsuit. We deny everything. It's as if we never existed.

CHAPTER 6

Wednesday, May 14, Year 1

One of our expert witnesses is no help, to say the least. Dr. Benedict Harris, a pathologist at Christian Hospital, looked at the slides at the request of Lowell. He thinks there are malignant cells in both of the Pap smears. Of course, this is very bad news, if not all that surprising, in view of retrospective bias. Let's face it, a lawyer brings in a couple of Pap smears for review, it's pretty obvious they are not going to be normal.

Then it goes from bad to disastrous. One of the cytotechnologists in his lab, a Ms. Arnold, says that our lab has a "terrible reputation"—that she interviewed with us for a job once upon a time, when she finished her cytotechnologist training, and was told by Dr. Spenser (me) that she would have to screen a minimum of one hundred Pap smears a day. That is against the law; one hundred Pap smears is the *maximum* number of slides a screener is allowed to screen in any twenty-four-hour period. That is the law of the land, as established by CLIA (Clinical Laboratory Improvement Act) legislation passed in 1988. Like every laboratory, we have measures in place to make sure that this hundred-slide limit is not surpassed. We have never insisted on a minimum number of slides to examine. We want our cytotechnologists to take their time and do it right.

What Ms. Arnold said is the most shocking lie that has ever been told about me. I can't get over it. It makes no sense. If we were doing such a thing, which we were not, and are not, I would be crazy to divulge this to a prospective employee on a job interview, someone I didn't even know. For all I knew at the time, the person could have been an undercover operative from the state or federal government checking up on me. No way would I take such a risk, of at least a fine and maybe worse.

I have no memory of Ms. Arnold. None.

What really gets me is that Dr. Benedict Harris believes her. He and I go way back. We were in medical school together and had much in common. We both loved sports, and we used to let off steam playing doubles handball—Benedict, one of my classmates, our pathology professor, and me. The four of us were pretty athletic. In high school, Benedict set state records in swimming and was a varsity swimmer at the Naval Academy. In high school, I was second in the state in tennis and played varsity tennis in college. We had great competitive games of handball. Benedict and I had some of the same friends and saw each other at parties from time to time. He was one class ahead of me, and he would give me information about what the next year for me would be like, and tips to survive. Benedict went into pathology, and I went into pathology. We were never great friends, but we got along well, and I had a high regard for him. I thought he had a high regard for me.

Evidently not. Benedict certainly had no reservations about passing on this slander to Lowell. It really hurts, that he would believe this about me and pass it on without getting my side of the story, which is that what Ms. Arnold is saying is a lie. Were someone to say this about Benedict, I would not believe it. That he would believe this of me shakes me to my core. It is so hard, maybe impossible, to see one 's self the way others see us. One of the teachings of semiotics is that it is impossible. Nevertheless, I go through life, showing up at work, doing the best I can every day, thinking that what I do is worthwhile, valuable, and rewarding, and well regarded, thinking that I am a respected member of the medical community and the community at large, and then this happens.

Lowell Pound, our lawyer, seems to regard this slander as credible in spite of the documentation we have sent him to the contrary. Maybe it's the source. If one was to take marble and sculpture the perfect-appearing physician/pathologist, it would be Benedict Harris. He is over six feet tall, handsome, blond, and fit—like he was at the Naval Academy where he was a cadet. After graduating, he served his country on nuclear submarines. After he left the Navy, he went to medical school. Then Benedict went into the private practice of pathology at one of the large downtown prestigious hospitals, where he quickly became pathology department chairman and laboratory director. He has led an exemplary life. Although we do not socialize, I run into him from time to time at meetings of some community medical committees I am on; he is usually the chairman. I see him at the North Texas Pathology meetings. He is on the committee at Mutual Malpractice to advise them about malpractice matters. So Lowell believes him as a credible source.

The movie *Rashomon* comforts me. For those of you who have not seen it, well, you should. A brief synopsis goes like this. The Japanese film plot device is that the same story (an apparent rape, robbery, and murder in preindustrial Japan) is told cinematically by four different narrators: the victim of the rape, her husband (who is murdered), the bandit, and a "neutral" observer, a woodcutter witness. The stories each tell vary widely in that they are different, biased, and even contradictory. But here's the thing: they are all true, at least to the person narrating the story. The message of the film is that there is no such thing as a reliable narrator.

Back to the events in this story, as being told by this narrator. Ms. Arnold is probably telling the truth as she sees it. Oh, heck, let's get rid of the "probably." She is telling the truth as she sees it. I'm certainly telling the truth as I see it. For example, I may have *said* "a maximum of one hundred slides," but she *heard* "a minimum of one hundred slides." Similarly, in her telling of the events of the interview, I am a "terrible" pathologist and we have a "terrible" lab. That is obviously not my view.

There is more bad news. Lowell also took the slides to Dr. Shelton, a pathologist at Catholic Hospital, for his interpretation. He too thinks we made a mistake and missed some atypical cells we should have seen. I should note that in my professional opinion, Dr. Shelton is an overrated pompous jerk.

I'm not surprised that Dr. Shelton saw some atypical cells. If an attorney brings some Pap smears to a pathologist for an opinion—what's he going to say? Nothing there? Doubtful. More likely the pathologist will meticulously go over the slide, cell by cell, until he finds an abnormal one. It would be interesting to know what would happen if Ms. Hawthorne's Pap smears were part of the usual working day of his laboratory and examined as part of that day's normal workload. That is the only true gauge of whether we missed something.

I have a clue about what would happen. Last year Dr. Gable, an internationally known expert on cytology (and who has indicated he will be a medical expert for us), did a very naughty experiment: At a workshop where he was lecturing on Pap smears, he distributed a collection of Pap smears and told the audience each smear was involved in Pap smear litigation for malpractice. He asked each audience member to look at the slides with the provided microscope and write down his diagnosis of the specimen, and the results were tabulated. Over half the audience called every Pap smear abnormal, and one specimen was regarded by 70% of the audience as having a very dangerous lesion. The punch line: it was a trick—none of the Pap smears were involved in litigation; each and every one of the Pap smears had been signed out as normal.

Tuesday, May 20, Year 1

My deposition is scheduled for July 10. Only Reynolds and I are scheduled for depositions, but my first rule of lawsuits is that nobody knows anything.

I am dreading the deposition. A deposition is part of the discovery portion of the lawsuit, which means the plaintiff's attorney can ask question after question about anything and everything under the sun, in the interests of supposedly discovering the facts of the case. That may be part of the purpose, but in my experience, they are a chance for the opposing attorney to abuse a witness. A deposition goes on for hours, or even days, boring question after boring question. My answers had better be good, because any mistake can be used against us at the trial.

I have testified at depositions and at trials. My experience is that testifying at trials is a lot easier. At a trial a judge and jury are present, and no one, including the plaintiff's attorney, can be obnoxious and abuse the witness, asking irrelevant questions. The judge and jury won't put up with it, and the last thing an attorney wants to do is tick off the judge and jury. Those safeguards are not in place at a deposition, and the attorney asking the questions can be as irritating as he wants, and a deposition can turn quite contentious.

In fact, that has happened to me with respect to Scott Francis, one of the plaintiff's lawyers in this case. I told Lowell that Scott Francis had deposed me in the past. I had been an expert witness called by the defense. The case was against a neurologist, and part of the case concerned some autopsy findings, and the defense wanted me to testify as an expert.

I testified at a deposition, conducted by Scott Francis, but not at the trial. There was a lot of conflict at the deposition. It got so bad that at one point Scott Francis was so exasperated that he asked the neurologist's attorneys to explain to me what a deposition was for. At the trial, the neurologist won, and Scott Francis's client didn't get a dime.

I am hoping the depositions happen soon. I want this case to be over.

Thursday, May 29 Year 1

Reynolds phoned me to tell me that our depositions are scheduled for July 10 and July 14. Also, Bruce Palmore and Billy Swenson, our two cytotechnologists, will have to give depositions. Interestingly, Lowell wants to put off their depositions until August, because by then the statute of limitations will run out, and Bruce and Billy cannot be sued.

"Why is Lowell so interested in protecting Bruce and Billy?" I asked.

"Maybe he doesn't want them to feel isolated and vindictive," said Reynolds. "If Bruce and Billy feel isolated and vindictive, they may turn on us to score points with the plaintiff or to get even."

"Good thinking."

Friday, May 30, Year 1

Where are we with respect to the lawsuit? There is a lot of what I call "revisionist history" going on, and Dr. John Pelton, a pathologist employee, is the biggest proponent. Today we talked on the phone, and he was ranting and raving to me about all the mistakes our cytotechnologists had made, particularly Billy—"two or three every day"—and how he would point this out to me and others, but people kept "blowing him off, and now the chickens are coming home to roost."

I said, "If I were you, I would stop that kind of talk right now. It does your cause no good to talk that way. If we lose a multimillion-dollar lawsuit and go out of business, you will be hurt along with everybody else."

"Well, I wouldn't say that to an attorney."

"I wouldn't say it to anyone, because what you are saying is not true. Yes, Billy makes some mistakes. So what!? I make mistakes, you make mistakes, and we *all* make mistakes. But no one, *including you,* ever documented that Billy was not a competent screener. Nor did anyone, *including you,* find or recruit someone better to do the job."

I don't blame John for being upset. He is named in the lawsuit, but he never saw the Pap smears in question, and he's not even one of the owners of the company. He had nothing to do with the matter. Obviously, he should be dropped from the lawsuit.

Until he is dropped, it is a nuisance to him. Every time John has to renew his state medical license or fill out the reapplication for medical staff privileges, he will have to answer the question "Since the last application have you been sued for malpractice, if so attach an explanation?" and he will have to answer yes and explain why he has been sued. The lawsuit is a hassle. He worries about having to give a deposition or testify at a trial.

I feel his pain. The thing about lawsuits is that they hang over you. They never take a day off. A lawsuit hangs around you at work, obviously, but it is also at the back of your mind every day—birthdays, wedding anniversaries, vacations—always.

So John should be dropped from the lawsuit and I should be dropped from the lawsuit. In fact, from my admittedly self-serving position, it is not fair that we are sued at all. Here's why: Pap smears are not a perfect test, never have been and never will be. Pap smears are not a *diagnostic* test, they are a *screening* test.

The Pap smear is arguably the best s*creening* test in the history of medicine, at least in terms of preventing cancer deaths. Dr. Papanicolaou worked on the test from 1926 to 1941. At that time the diagnosis of cervical cancer or precursors of cancer could only be made by looking at a piece of cervical cancer under the microscope. The gynecologist had to do an operation to get a piece of tissue (biopsy), and the pathologists would take that tissue, fix it , process it, and look at the resultant slides under the microscope—a labor-intensive procedure, for sure, and low yield as well, because the only tissue sampled is what the gynecologist could see and biopsy. Not surprisingly, the rate of early detection, diagnosis, and cure of cervical cancer was quite low. Dr. Papanicolaou's idea was to look at a vaginal smear instead, and thus be able to look at large numbers of cells from a large number of patients. Thus, he thought that cervical cancer, or its precursor, could be detected early enough to cure.

Dr. Papanicolaou was right. Since the Pap smear was first introduced in 1941, cervical cancer death rates have dropped by 70% according to the American Cancer Society. This year approximately 4,800 women will die in the United States from cervical cancer, compared with 26,000 in 1941.

In a sense, the Pap smear has been too successful, in that there has been a tendency to regard any death of a woman from cervical cancer who has had routine Pap smears as malpractice. This may not be fair. I have been repeatedly emphasizing to anyone who will listen that this is a screening laboratory test and, like any laboratory test, is not perfect. In fact, studies have shown that there is an apparently irreducible false negative rate of 5-10%, which means that out of every one hundred women with cervical abnormities that should be detected by the Pap smear, there will be five to ten who will be missed. Studies show that this happens at all laboratories, even the best. Is this because of poor screening by the cytotechnologist, where abnormal cells are missed, or because the cells appear normal on the slide, or because the vagina/cervix was not adequately sampled? Who knows? My conjecture is that the explanation is that all the steps involved in Pap smear collection and interpretation are done by humans, and humans are not perfect.

Pap smear malpractice suits are on the rise. At one malpractice insurer in the last two years there were fifty-six claims in which Pap smears were the central issue. At that company the number of claims for cases involving Pap smears has tripled in the last three years.

Wednesday, June 11, Year 1

I was home, on my day off. My partner Reynolds phoned me three times:

First call: He told me that Lowell, our attorney, met recently with Bruce Palmore and Billy Swenson, the two cytotechnologists. Bruce is "like a ferret caught in a cage," going crazy with stress and anxiety. Somehow Bruce thought he was being called in to be commended for catching something Billy missed, and that he was going to be given an award or something. Bruce about lost it when he found out that *he* had missed something on one of the slides.

I'm mystified about that. I told Bruce several months ago that he was involved in the litigation. I guess he was in denial.

Second call: Reynolds had panic in his voice. Today he received the plaintiff's interrogatories, which were sent to Lowell. Interrogatories are questions from the other side that our side has to answer. Lowell will need our help with the answers, particularly regarding the medical/scientific questions. Reynolds is leaving town tomorrow. Can he leave them for me to take care of?

Yes.

Third call: Reynolds has received more material from the plaintiff, this time answers to our interrogatories (i.e., questions) that we asked the plaintiff. Reynolds wants me to look them over. I said I would.

"I don't want this to go to trial," he said. "I'd settle for a million dollars or less."

So would I.

Thursday, June 12, Year 1

John Pelton phoned me today. "I received a renewal application for my Texas Medical License. There is a question that asks whether or not I have been sued in the past year. Do I have to answer yes?"

"I don't think you have any choice but to answer yes," I said. "Get used to it. You'll have to answer that question a lot."

"How will I explain it?"

"With the truth—something like I am involved in litigation about an alleged misdiagnosis of some Pap smears. I did not examine the slides in question, and I plan a vigorous defense."

I started answering the interrogatories today, a lot of work. Bruce Palmore, the cytotechnologist who is like a "ferret in a cage," phoned me today.

"The lawsuit has really shaken me up," he said. "I can't eat, I can't sleep… I just feel terrible about missing a slide. No Knute Rockne speech is going to cheer me up. That '5% irreducible error rate of false negatives' doesn't cut it for me."

I didn't cheer him up. I'm not Knute Rockne.

It was a busy day. As I promised Reynolds, I looked over the answers of the plaintiff to *our* interrogatories. Lowell phoned me today to find out what I thought of them. "Were there any significant injuries the plaintiff suffered?" he asked.

"Yes, things could not be much worse," I answered.

I am not overstating. The medical injuries are gruesome. As if that were not bad enough, according to the interrogatory responses, as I write these words, Lynn Hawthorne is in Ivory Hospital for a "total pelvic exenteration" for recurrent tumor, a horrible desperate operation including removal of the urinary bladder, vagina, rectum, adjacent soft tissues and lymph nodes. When I was a medical student, I participated in one of these operations, which started early in the morning, around 7, lasted all day, and was not over until past midnight.

Did I do enough to prevent this terrible outcome for this patient? Was I a good enough manager? Did I have enough skill to recruit good cytotechnologists to work for us? Would it have made a difference? Does our laboratory do enough good to compensate for the shortcomings?

I am not wise enough to know. I am tired, though, very tired.

CHAPTER 7

Friday, June 13, Year 1

I chucked it all to be a screenwriter. I'm only forty-seven years old, an unusual age to change careers, but I have been discontented with medicine and pathology for several months. The constituencies I have include patients, other physicians, laboratory technologists, hospital administrators, nurses, insurance companies, thirty employees, and patients. I have to answer to inspection authorities from the state, the Joint Commission on Accreditation for Hospitals, the American Association of Blood Banks, the College of American Pathologists, and others who are looking over my shoulder. Keeping all of them happy all the time is impossible. The thing that gets to me most, though, is the unrelenting pressure and stress.

There are the administrative duties involved in owning a several-million-dollar in revenue company, and being the laboratory director at two hospitals. Every day I dissect several dozen specimens, look at hundreds of tissue slides, review twenty or thirty peripheral blood smears, and review ten to twenty Pap smears. The stakes are tremendous, life and death, and a mistake can result in a several-million-dollar lawsuit. During my career in medicine, I have seen the role of physician in our "health care system" change gradually from leader to target. For several months before this lawsuit, I have been burnt out, and many times I have said, "One more lawsuit and I'm gone." The lawsuit arrived, and I'm gone.

To summarize this lawsuit, I am being sued for $10 million by a woman I never met about some Pap smears I never saw. A woman I have no memory of, Ms. Arnold, has said terrible things about me and my lab, which are lies. A pathologist, who I thought was my friend, passed on these falsehoods to our attorney, who believes them.

I think it's time to quit.

So, today, on Friday the thirteenth, I resigned from my practice effective September 11, ninety days from now. Hopefully that will give my partners enough time to adjust, and adjust they will. I am not indispensable. No one is. As Charles de Gaulle said—the cemeteries are full of indispensable men. I predict I will be missed, but not as a pathologist; others will take my place and do what I do. I handle the inspections. Someone else will do that. I take care of personnel. Someone else will do that. I serve as chairman of the pathology department and laboratory director at two of our three hospitals. Someone else will do that.

What the people I work with may miss… is me.

Reynolds Price is out of town, so I left him a message on his phone that I was quitting. I phoned my other partner, Dr. Larry Roundtree, and told him the news that I was resigning. He tried to talk me out of it. "You're letting this peripheral stuff bother you too much. I hate to see the waste of a great talent."

Later in the day I told Lowell Powell that I was resigning, and that my last day of work would be September 11. "Larry and Reynolds will be surprised," he said.

"Larry sure was."

Over the phone I went over the plaintiff's answers to our interrogatories. I told Lowell that the medical prognosis of Lynn Hawthorne is dismal, and about her medical condition, things could not be much worse. She is going to die from this cancer sooner or later and probably sooner.

I can't rationalize what happened. I know that the Pap smear is a screening test, not perfect, and I know the statistics about false negatives, and most importantly, *I didn't see the slides*, which I keep telling myself. I am still bothered by what happened, bothered enough to quit.

Monday, June 16, Year 1

I received another letter from Lowell Pound. He showed the Pap smears to yet another pathologist, Dr. Rob Hall from a private practice group here in town, our main competitors. Dr. Hall thought the slides in question had atypical cells characteristic of a high-grade lesion. Again, no help for us. I am impressed at the efforts Lowell is making on our behalf.

Tuesday, June 17, Year 1

I received another letter from Lowell. My deposition scheduled for July has been postponed, because Lowell has a conflict at that time.

This is so typical. As a pathologist, a scientist, it kills me that nothing regarding a lawsuit is definite. Such a contrast to the way I live and practice. For example, if I make a diagnosis of small cell carcinoma on a lung biopsy, that patient will die. At the present time, that is a fact, count on it—terribly horribly unfortunate, but true. But in law, nothing is definite. A deposition scheduled for July may or may not happen in July. A trial date means that the trial may or may not happen then. This case may or may not be settled. My first rule of lawsuits remains: nobody knows anything.

Now Reynolds Price and I are scheduled to give our depositions on September 16. Billy Swenson and Bruce Palmore will give their depositions on September 15.

It was up to me to phone Billy and Bruce with the news. Bruce's voice quavered as he talked. Billy was surprisingly friendly.

Wednesday, June 18, Year 1

Lowell phoned this afternoon to make sure it was okay for him to inform Milton Jackson, the attorney for Mutual Malpractice, that I was leaving pathology and medicine. Lowell is drafting a letter to send Mr. Jackson updating him about the case, which sounds reasonable, since they are paying the bills. Lowell thinks my leaving medicine is an important development.

"It's okay with me," I said. "I've already told Larry, and I left a message on Reynolds's recorder (he is still out of town), and I sent him a letter."

Lowell and I discussed the case. It does not look good for our defense for these reasons:

First, we are going to have two slides that no one is going to call normal. We can persuade the jury that we have the highest quality lab in North America (a Quixotic task), and we are still going to have to defend the fact that we misdiagnosed two slides.

Second, our case to the jury that we are a high-quality lab will certainly be disputed by the plaintiff's attorneys, who will take some facts out of context, distort them, and make our laboratory look bad.

Third, what I regard as the most salient point of our defense, that a Pap smear is a screening test and not a diagnostic test, will be difficult for a jury to understand. A false negative is when a person has the disease, but the test for the disease does not pick it up. Most lab tests have false negative results, and the Pap smear is well known to have limitations, with resultant false negatives for numerous reasons:

1. The cervical lesion may not be sampled by the gynecologist.

2. The lesion may be sampled, but the cells are missed by the screener.

3. Errors happen.

4. The personnel involved are not perfect.

"I'm not even sure Reynolds understands what a false negative is," I said to Lowell. "And if even a trained pathologist like Reynolds doesn't understand the concept, how will we get a jury to understand?"

"I think it will be tough," said Lowell.

"I'm not sure a jury will care, even if they understand."

"Yeah."

"I am interested in settling the case. Any timetable for that?"

"After the deposition. All the medical facts need to come out first, and let's see if anyone sat on this lady's symptoms for a long time. The settlement will be this fall at the earliest."

"I'm sure willing to settle."

"That's why you have insurance."

Thursday, June 19, Year 1

Today I received a copy of the letter Lowell sent to Milton Jackson. Wow, that was fast. Just a couple of days ago Lowell was telling me what I thought were his preliminary thoughts, but then before the week is out, I get the update.

In the letter Lowell points out that there is no way to defend the diagnoses of Billy and Bruce. About the plaintiff's medical condition Lowell quotes me: "Things could not be much worse."

Lowell ends the letter this way: "Finally, I want you to know that Jack Spenser has informed me that he is resigning from Pathology Services, P.C., effective at the end of the summer. Apparently, he has had enough of the practice of pathology; he intends to enroll at the Dallas Film Institute in the next month or two and cease the practice of pathology."

That pretty much covers it. Lawyers do have a way with words. Good lawyers (and Lowell is a good lawyer) are good storytellers. I don't think it's a coincidence that Scott Turow, John Grisham, and Louis Auchincloss were attorneys before they became noted authors. There are probably several reasons for this. The day-to-day work of an attorney involves writing, and the writing has to be true and accurate—a last will and testament had better say exactly what the client wants to happen or the heirs will bring their own interpretations. A good lawyer also has to be a good storyteller—the jury will believe the side that presents the best story.

Lowell recommends "that this is a case that should be presented to the Claims Review Committee as soon as possible."

Friday, June 20, Year 1

Today I worked on the answers to some of the plaintiff's interrogatories. The questions are tricky. For example, there are questions about how we do quality assurance and quality control. What to include is not all that obvious. The documents pertaining to quality assurance and quality control would fill several closets—it would take a moving van to transport everything. As it is, our employees are working hard to help me find the pertinent records and photocopying them. Then I am trying to organize them and get them ready to send to Lowell.

Today I finally talked to Reynolds and told him I was resigning. He wasn't surprised. He wants to get together to prepare for our depositions, which I think is a good idea.

I phoned Mutual Malpractice to find out about getting tail malpractice insurance, which is what you buy to cover malpractice claims that are filed *after* you leave your practice. It will cost $4,500.

Wednesday, June 25, Year 1

More bad news. Lynn Hawthorne's health is now so bad that she is leaving our community to go live with her parents in Iowa City, Iowa, her hometown. She cannot take care of herself anymore. Her deposition is scheduled for July 14. Reynolds and I will attend.

"Lowell is really down," said Reynolds. "I asked him about why he made such a big deal out of the fact that you are leaving medicine. Lowell answered that the plaintiff's attorneys would try to make you out as some kind of a flake, leaving medicine to write screenplays."

"I am some kind of a flake," I said.

"Evidently I am as well," said Reynolds. "I told Lowell I'm halfway out the door. Lowell said that *he* wouldn't mind quitting."

"I guess everyone is burnt out."

"I'm suspicious of the whole thing," said Reynolds. "I think the plaintiff is just tired of working and wants to retire at our expense."

"I disagree," I said. "I think she is that sick."

Thursday, June 26, Year 1

Today I finished our responses to the plaintiff's interrogatories. I needed a lot of help from several people to find the applicable documents. Everyone speaks with an anxious voice whenever the subject of the lawsuit comes up.

A lawsuit is like an earthquake, shaking everything to its foundations. A lawsuit is also a magnifying glass, looking at everything in my professional life. Everything that can be asked about the Pap smears, and the lab that read the Pap smears, and those who work at the lab, including me, will be asked, and the answers carefully examined. Not just my professional life, but my entire life will be carefully examined. My experience has been that at the deposition I will be asked everything under the sun. Were I divorced, there would be questions about that. Had I done military service, there would be questions about that. My entire life will be investigated. Where I live, where I go to church, any trouble with the law, anything at all is fair game in the discovery phase of a lawsuit.

At least this set of interrogatory answers is done. I will send them to Lowell.

Friday, June 27, Year 1

Reynolds phoned. He has reviewed our interrogatory responses. "I wouldn't change a thing," he said.

I asked about getting our individual names dropped from the lawsuit. Ain't gonna happen. Why drop deep pockets? Rhetorical question.

Thursday, July 3, Year 1

Today Reynolds gave me his take on the plaintiff responses to our interrogatories. "You noticed that she was in a *ménage a trois,*" he said.

"No, I missed that."

"There is a significant other who is not her husband."

"Yeah, but I don't think it was a *ménage a trois.*"

"I'm tellin' you, Jack, we are taking the fall for everyone in this case. All her problems are from the surgery and radiation treatments. Dr. Helen Smith over at Ivory botched the operation and told the patient we screwed up, just to keep the patient from suing her."

"I think you're right."

"She had a vaginal discharge, which everyone ignored. She also had condylomatous changes. She was seen at Pinnacle Hospital Emergency Room, where her complaints were blown off as rectal abscess rather than cancer. We are taking the hits for all of this."

"I saw that."

"We deserve to take some of the hit, but we shouldn't be taking all the hit for failures of managed care, for screeners missing slides…"

He's right. It's not fair, but life is not fair, thank goodness. I sure hope I don't get what I deserve. I am sure Lynn Hawthorne, single mom dying of cervical cancer, thinks that life is not fair. Were I in her shoes, a single mom with limited resources, I would be doing everything in my power to protect my kid and get her the money needed to raise her. And if I sued the wrong guys and hurt some innocent people in the process, tough.

Tuesday, July 8, Year 1

I received a letter from Lowell today. I wanted to talk to him about it, but his assistant told me that he is out of town trying a case. I'm irritated and amazed at how self-centered I can be, thinking my case is not only the most important case Lowell has, but the only case.

My interpretation of Lowell's letter is that Lynn Hawthorne is dying, according to her attorney, Scott Francis. Therefore Mr. Francis wants her to give an "Evidentiary Deposition" before she dies, at which Mr. Francis will ask the questions. Lowell objects and wants her to give a regular deposition so that Lowell can ask questions as well. This has to be sorted out by Monday.

By phone I talked to my partner Dr. Larry Roundtree this morning. He is in agreement with Reynolds and me that he is ready to settle—the earlier, the better. Like Reynolds, he is skeptical about the whole thing. He thinks the plaintiff is holding out on the evidence. For example, we know that Lynn Hawthorne was seen by Dr. Ken Emry, one of our local family practitioners, and his nurse practitioner. We have yet to see any of those records.

I worked last Saturday and talked to Bruce Palmore. He is a short guy like me, but unlike me, he is pretty much bald. There is stress all over his face. The case continues to haunt him. He keeps a copy of the lawsuit posted where he screens Pap smears, to remind him of the stakes: life and death.

Friday, July 11, Year 1

Reynolds talked to Lowell by phone today, and then Reynolds phoned me. We have finally received the rest of the medical records of the plaintiff, about seventy-two hours before her deposition on Monday. The records are those of Dr. Ken Emry, family physician, and according to Reynolds, they are a "paean to everything wrong with managed care," and after looking at them myself, I agree.

During at least half the clinic visits, Lynn Hawthorne did not see Dr. Emry at all, only his nurse practitioner. As far as the records show, between the two of them they did about every lab test and X-ray study known to medicine, but did not do the one thing that might have helped—a pelvic exam of the patient. The cervical cancer would have been seen if anybody looked, and diagnosed earlier by a tissue biopsy.

Even a Pap smear collecting cells directly from the cervical mass might have rendered enough abnormal cells to be detected by a screener and a pathologist, with an earlier diagnosis. In summary, it would have been nice to receive a biopsy of the cervical mass, which would have been a *diagnostic* test rather than a Pap smear *screening* test. The cervical biopsy finally done by Dr. Bishop, Ms. Hawthorne's gynecologist, was sent to us and, in fact, was diagnostic, but it should have happened earlier.

There's been a schedule change regarding the plaintiff's depositions. The evidentiary deposition will be a week from Monday, conducted by Scott Francis, but Lowell's regular deposition, when he will ask the questions, is set for this Monday, at the office of Scott Francis. Reynolds is ticked off about this. According to Reynolds, he and Lowell had some heated words. I think the stress is getting to Reynolds, as well as Bruce Palmore. Me too.

I asked Reynolds why he was so upset about the depositions. His contention is that with respect to the timing, we have been "completely outmaneuvered in all this, that only now, seventy-two hours before the deposition, have we finally gotten the records we need," which does not give Reynolds, me, or Lowell enough time to prepare for the deposition.

Lowell answered all this by saying Reynolds could get another attorney if he was not satisfied by the way Lowell was representing him.

Reynolds continues to be very skeptical of the plaintiff and her attorney. "I wonder if she is really as sick as she claims?" he asked me.

Monday we'll find out.

CHAPTER 8

Monday, July 14, Year 1

Today, approximately five months after the lawsuit was filed, I finally met the plaintiff, Lynn Hawthorne. Her deposition took place this morning at the office of Lichty, Francis, and Associates, located right smack-dab in the center of University Park, the wealthiest part of the city, across the street from the Botanical Gardens. The law office looks like an old mansion, which it once was, rather than a law office. In fact, it's as nice as the mansion in Botanical Gardens, maybe nicer. It's the kind of beautiful house a plutocrat would have.

I was the first to arrive. The front door was locked, so I waited on the porch. It was a sunny day, warm but not hot, quite pleasant actually. Eventually Scott Francis, Lynn Hawthorne's attorney, arrived with a woman I assumed to be the Ms. Hawthorne. I recognized Scott Francis from the time he had previously deposed me. Scott Francis must be in his forties. He has a soft voice and thin blond hair, which he combs to the left. He is slim and wiry, like a varsity tennis player or a history professor. On first look, he appears slight and short, but when I stood next to him, I discovered he is actually tall, around six feet two inches or so. I recognized Scott Francis from a previous deposition, but he didn't remember me. I introduced myself. We were both dressed in dark suits.

Mr. Francis, the unidentified woman, and I stepped into a short hallway. To my left was a reception area with a low oval coffee table on which there were many magazines, and the woman walked there.

"This is Lynn Hawthorne," said Mr. Francis.

"Hello," I said.

She said nothing. Lynn Hawthorne is thirty-six years old, very slim, with hazel eyes and long light-brown hair, so light that it is almost gray. She wore her hair long, combed straight back to reach her shoulders. She was dressed in a maroon jacket over a loose-fitting blue denim dress, which went down to her ankles, where it met the top of black sandals with thick straps. She wore long earrings. She is a little taller than me, about five feet seven inches or so.

Outside, a car started honking repeatedly, signifying that a car alarm had gone off. Mr. Francis and I went outside to see what was happening. Ms. Hawthorne stayed inside. A car with Iowa license plates was making the racket—horn sounding and lights flashing, signifying an alarm, which in this case was evidently a false alarm. A woman with the age and appearance to be Lynn Hawthorne's mother was trying to turn off the alarm. Scott Francis went to help her. I stayed on the porch, waiting for Lowell Pound and Reynolds Price.

They finally showed up. Of course, I've known Reynolds Price, my partner, for fifteen years. He is in his mid-fifties, tall, slim, and fit. He has a lean face with gray hair, gray eyes, and even his skin is reminiscent of gray—he moves quickly and fast—the overall appearance is that of a gray wolf. He usually has a knowing cynical look, not unpleasant, an expression that says this is an amusing crazy world we live in.

This was my first look at Lowell Pound, although I had talked to him many times on the phone, and he has a most pleasant baritone voice, mild and calm. In person he is anything but mild appearing. He is a block of a man, about six feet two inches, strong, who looks like a marine, because that's what he once was, and he looks like a Southern Methodist University football team lineman, because that's what he once was. Lowell is about my age, in his mid to late forties. He's bald for the most part, farther along in that respect than Scott Francis. His remaining hair is red, but graying. He has prominent red eyebrows. His legs are not particularly long and bow a little. Lowell walks rapidly and leans forward as he walks, like a varsity wrestler entering the ring, which I was in high school.

We introduced ourselves to each other. We had some privacy on the porch. "I mainly wanted you here to meet the plaintiff," Lowell said to Reynolds and me. "At this deposition, I'm mainly going to ask her a bunch of financial questions." Then we went inside.

The court stenographer, a short blonde woman, arrived to complete our group. We assembled in the conference room, which must have been the dining room at one time, around a long oval wood table. On one wall there was a picture of Dwight Eisenhower. Even before we started, Lynn Hawthorne seemed very subdued and weak. As everyone helped themselves to coffee, she said, "Usually I don't drink coffee, but I was very tired this morning."

The court stenographer said, "Do you promise to tell the truth, the whole truth, and nothing but the truth, so help you God?"

"I do," said Ms. Hawthorne, and we were underway. She was an impressive, sincere, cooperative witness, so cooperative that she sometimes answered the questions before Lowell had finished asking them. Mr. Francis and Lowell both had to ask her to stop doing that. She answered all the questions in a soft voice, with little emotion, almost in a monotone, like she was in shock—and considering what has happened to her, she probably is.

What struck me, though, as she answered questions and told her medical history, is that nothing anyone did helped this unfortunate patient. In spite of our alleged screw-up with the Pap smear, her cervical cancer was only the size of a little fingertip when it was discovered, and with her first operation she should have been cured. She wasn't. After her second operation, she should have been cured, but she wasn't, nor was she cured after her third operation, when the cancer should have been completely removed. None of the operations she'd endured helped. The subsequent radiation therapy did not help. *Nothing* helped.

Lynn Hawthorne is quite attractive, even after all she's been through. Since her divorce two years ago from the father of her eight-year-old daughter, her testimony is that she has had three sex partners. During a recess, I mentioned her good looks to Reynolds. "That's what got her in trouble," he replied, alluding to her apparently sexually transmitted human papillomavirus (HPV) infection, which activated oncogenes, which eventually turned her normal cervical cells into cancer. The fact that this happened is more evidence of the horribly bad luck she has experienced. HPV is ubiquitous, with millions of new infections every year. In almost every case, the infection spontaneously disappears, with no ill effects, but infection and its consequences will kill the incredibly unfortunate Lynn Hawthorne.

According to her testimony, Ms. Hawthorne said she divorced her husband because he was a drug addict and stole cars. She has sole custody of her daughter, eight-year-old Tara. Her ex-husband has only supervised contact with his daughter.

I can't blame Ms. Hawthorne for going after us, or after somebody, to give her money. She is going to die, and there will be no resources to take care of her daughter. Raising her is going to take money, and Ms. Hawthorne has little to none. Her ex-husband and the father of Tara will be no help. If it takes a lawsuit to get the money she needs, well, so be it. She will fight for her daughter.

Ms. Hawthorne is pointing the finger at us. She is not the only one. "The Pap smear slides had been under read," said Dr. Bishop, her ob/gyn physician, after finally seeing the small cervical cancer and doing the biopsy. Dr. Smith, her oncologist at Ivory Hospital, who did the follow-up surgery, felt obligated to point out that her cervical cancer "should have shown up in her last two Pap smears."

Interestingly, Lynn Hawthorne has a medical background; she has been supporting herself as a radiology technician specializing in mammography. For a time she worked at Pinnacle Hospital, one of the hospitals where we provide pathology services. Two physician radiologists she worked with (I know and work with both of them) "encouraged her to bring litigation."

In summary, four of my colleagues, fellow physicians, ALL decided that we at Pathology Services had messed up, and encouraged this patient to sue us, without getting our side of the story, looking at the Pap smears themselves, or having an independent expert look at the Pap smears.

During another break, Lowell, Reynolds, and I were on the porch, talking. Lowell said, "Do you have any questions you want me to ask?"

Actually, I did. I took a yellow legal pad out of my briefcase, which had questions I had worked on over the weekend. Lowell looked at the first few and liked them. "Let's see what else you've got," he said.

My thinking was that since Ms. Hawthorne's background was in radiology, she should be familiar with the concept of false negatives. For example, mammography has a certain rate of false negatives, and not every breast cancer is discovered by mammography studies, which are screening tests, not diagnostic tests. If there is a mammographic abnormality, the diagnostic study is a tissue follow-up by breast biopsy or excision of the lesion. The concepts regarding Pap smears are the same.

A Pap smear is a screening test, with a certain rate of false negatives, and not every cervical cancer is picked up by Pap smears; if there is an abnormality on a Pap smear, the follow-up diagnostic test is a biopsy or excision of the cervical lesion. The goal of my questions was to see if Ms. Hawthorne might concede that, just as there are times when a woman has breast cancer but the mammography is normal, there are times a patient has cervical cancer but the Pap smear is normal. Here's the way it went:

"There is a recognized false negative rate for mammography, is there not?" asked Lowell.

"Yes," Lynn Hawthorne answered.

"And is it also your understanding that there is a recognized false negative rate for Pap smears as well?"

"Yes."

Later Lowell said, "We got some pretty good answers out of your questions."

That's about as good as it got for our side. Like Lowell said at the beginning, most of the questions were financial—going over tax returns, mortgage payments, grocery bills, car payments, insurance coverage, and all the nuisance things we all have to do to stay alive.

Here are the other things we learned, from her honest, sincere deposition:

1. Lynn Hawthorne has a good work ethic. She joined the Air Force twelve years ago. Once she completed her initial training, she had an obligation to the National Guard, where her main specialty was air traffic control.

2. She has worked as an X-ray technologist at two hospitals: Pinnacle Radiology Group, which is based at one of the hospitals we cover, and Ivory Medical Center, one of the academic/medical school institutions in our city.

3. When she was diagnosed with cancer, she was working on a master's degree in business administration in addition to working full time. Eventually she would like to have some management skills so she can stop being a bedside technologist and "get off my feet." Sounds reasonable.

4. Ms. Hawthorne and her ex-husband were divorced because of irreconcilable differences and due to his drug use. Also, her ex-husband had been arrested at least twice for taking a car and not returning it. He has had little or no contact with his daughter.

5. Dr. Smith at Ivory Hospital told her that after her first surgery, after we allegedly messed up on the Pap smears, that she still had a "93–95%" good prognosis.

The deposition finished about noon. Lowell, Reynolds, and I sought privacy again on the porch. Lowell talked about settling the case. "It will only get worse for us," he said, "unless she dies, and if she dies, you know who they will bring to the jury—an eight-year-old girl, Tara, to take the stand. It is better to settle now, give her some peace of mind, and give us some peace of mind."

Lowell is preaching to the choir. No one wants to settle the case more than me.

Reynolds and I went to the North Dallas Cafeteria to get some lunch. As we drove away, Lowell and Scott Francis were on the porch, standing and talking.

Reynolds had an agenda at lunch, trying to convince me not to leave the practice of medicine and pathology—he said I "need to continue working, at least part time, and I need the mental stimulation to stay sharp."

He could be right, but I'm gone.

Tuesday, July 15, Year 1

I plan to go to Lynn Hawthorne's evidentiary deposition next Monday. At that deposition her attorney, Scott Francis, will be doing the questioning, and it will be taped for the jury to see, in case Lynn Hawthorne is deceased by the time of the trial, which unfortunately is looking likely.

Reynolds phoned me today. He and Lowell continue to not get along. "Things have gotten so bad," said Reynolds, "that Lowell thinks I need to join a support group of physicians who have been sued. For all I know, you agree."

"I don't think you need to join a support group," I said.

I called Lowell to tell him that I would be attending Ms. Hawthorne's deposition. "I want to settle this case," I said. "Having met her, and seen her at her deposition, Lynn Hawthorne does not strike me as a vindictive person; she just wants to take care of herself and her child. I don't know about Scott Francis, whether he is going to be greedy or not. Anyway, I am ready to settle this case on anything remotely resembling reasonable terms."

"It's not up to Francis," said Lowell. "It will be up to his boss, Dale Lichty, who is as greedy as they come."

Wednesday, July 16, Year 1

Today I was at Rural Hospital when I got beeped. It was Lowell. The evidentiary deposition scheduled for Monday is off, because Lynn Hawthorne is having more surgery.

And that's how quickly things change, in less than twenty-four hours. My first rule of lawsuits: nobody knows anything.

CHAPTER 9

Friday, July 18, Year 1

Dr. Larry Roundtree, President of Pathology Services, P.C., sent a letter to Lowell Pound authorizing him to settle the case.

Wednesday, July 23, Year 1

Reynolds phoned me several times today. At a meeting of the Mutual Malpractice Board last night, Benedict Harris, the pathologist from Christian Hospital and member of the board, recommended that we settle the case. Dr. Harris said that he is "sure they have similar cases" in their files at Christian Hospital, but nevertheless we should settle the case.

What is unsettling is that Dr. Harris continues to spread the slander about me and our laboratory: Lowell continues to hear from Dr. Harris about Ms. Arnold in his laboratory who says that we have a "bad reputation." She's sticking to her story. In fact, she's padded it. Now the latest is that she was interviewed for a job at our laboratory and interviewed by "Jack Spenser" (me), who offered her a job and told her that she would have to screen "more than one hundred slides a day."

That continues to be an outright lie, which I unequivocally deny.

It is interesting that the story has changed. It was "at least one hundred slides a day" and now it is "more than one hundred slides a day." Either policy would be against the law. The Clinical Laboratory Improvement Act sets a limit of one hundred slides a day, with documentation requirements that this limit not be exceeded. It would be professional suicide to propose this to one of my trusted employees, let alone a stranger applying for a job. Plus, I obey the law. I have had two minor traffic tickets, ever. Other than that, I have never been in trouble with anybody. I am one of those persons who obeys the rules. This lawsuit is proving to me that you can obey the rules, do the right thing, but that is no guarantee things will go your way.

Now I am being slandered by a woman I have no recollection of meeting. I phoned Lowell, and his demeanor as he passes on these lies is very matter of fact, and as far as I can tell, he has not contested these allegations to anyone. In fact, my impression is that he believes them, in spite of my statements and documentation to the contrary, which I have given him in response to the plaintiff's interrogatories. Categorically, we do not and never have had a quota for a number of slides a cytotechnologist has to screen, and certainly have not required one hundred slides or more than one hundred slides per day be screened.

I have no recollection of interviewing Ms. Arnold, offering her a job, or even meeting her or ever encountering her. Our lab has no records of any contact with her, and we've looked. Ms. Arnold, Dr. Harris, and Lowell have presented no documentation whatsoever for her allegations, other than her blabbing about it—no written records, no recordings, no witnesses, NOTHING OTHER THAN HER UNCORROBORATED ORAL STATEMENTS.

I'm in an episode of *The Twilight Zone*. Until now, I thought I had a good reputation and our lab did too. This lawsuit has come out of nowhere, and now this slander is coming out of nowhere. How do I defend myself? I always thought the truth would win out, but I don't think that anymore. I also thought I would have enough credibility that people would believe me, especially about medicine and pathology. I've paid my dues, earned my way into medical school, learned my pathology craft in residency, gotten years of experience under my belt, always trying to do my best every day, with every specimen, with every administrative decision, with every hiring decision, and doing my best for our patients. This is my reward!? To be told in the lawsuit and by my colleagues that my lab and I are terrible with a bad reputation.

Thursday, July 24, Year 1

I talked to Lowell twice today. He sounds really down. I think he is having a midlife crisis, like me. I wonder to him whether my actions to chuck it all and be a screenwriter will affect the case. "Will I be perceived as a flake?" I asked.

"I would not use the word 'flake,' but what you are doing is a fact we will have to deal with," he said.

"I am amused at that anyone should try to talk me out of leaving medicine, and say I am a flake. I think a flake would stay in a field where he could get sued for ten million dollars by a woman he never met, for slides he never saw."

"I think you are doing what a lot of people would like to do, but don't have the courage."

I told Lowell that I thought Dr. Harris would be a good expert witness for us, even though he has an employee who thinks we run a bad lab, and I am the chief culprit. I told Lowell that I still have absolutely no memories of this Ms. Arnold.

I'm less than thirty days from leaving medicine.

Wednesday, July 30, Year 1

I talked to Reynolds. We are going to send Lynn Hawthorne's Pap smears to the Medical University of South Carolina for another review. It will be a blind independent review, different from any review that has been done so far on the slides. The methods were described in a recent *Laboratory Medicine* journal article: Their cytology department does something very interesting, and actually kind of naughty. What they do is remove the retrospective bias that occurs when a Pap smear involved in litigation is taken to a "neutral expert" for review. What the South Carolina lab does is take Pap smears that are involved in litigation, like ours, and "bury" the slides in their laboratory's routine daily workload, labeling the slides in question as one of their own, so the slides in question look exactly like every other Pap smear to be screened, thus getting rid of retrospective bias. A report is then rendered. This process is repeated ten times until a total of ten supervisor-level cytotechnologists look at each slide, and the results are tabulated. They have agreed to do this study on Ms. Hawthorne's Pap smears. So our Pap smears should finally have a good, unbiased review—which is what we have not had. Every review of our Pap smears so far has involved Lowell schlepping the Pap smears to a pathologist who obviously knows something is up, and does not want to be the one to "miss" something, so "abnormal cells" are found. The Medical University of South Carolina is doing this neutral unbiased study to help the profession and get some justice. If, in fact, the Pap smear is abnormal, their review should confirm it, and justice can be done by the defendant making a settlement, *but* if the Pap smear is normal with their approach, that should help the defense get some justice, proving the defendants did nothing wrong.

About time somebody did something. Pap smear litigation may turn into a national crisis, and I am not the only one who thinks so. I recently heard National Public Radio telling the story of the Pap smear litigation "crisis," and one of the commentators said that "the Pap smear is a screening test, not a diagnostic test," which is what I have been pounding the table about for the last several months. The narrator said that "if Pap smear litigation continued, access of women to this great test would be hampered, because people would stop doing the test due to the potential liability. Unless there was some sanity soon, there would be some casualties."

Discussing this, Reynolds said to me, "I know of one already."

Friday, August 1, Year 1

I received a letter from Lowell Pound. Ms. Hawthorne has moved to her hometown—Iowa City, Iowa—so it will be necessary to take her next deposition there.

Monday, August 4, Year 1

Today I received another letter from Lowell. With each one I take a deep breath. The letters never have good news. It was another set of interrogatories to answer, which means I will have to answer them. I have spent days of my life running down documents and answers for these interrogatories.

Lowell is going to Iowa City to hear Ms. Hawthorne's evidentiary deposition. He doesn't think that any of us, the defendants, need to attend.

Just as I was opening the letter from Lowell, I was called to the operating suite by Mary Bishop, Ms. Hawthorne's gynecologist, who needed me to do a frozen section diagnosis on a specimen she had just removed from a patient. It took me the usual twenty minutes or so to come up with a diagnosis, and wearing my scrubs, I ran up the stairs to give Dr. Bishop the results. I was face-to-face with her for the first time since the lawsuit by her patient was filed. There seemed to be a chill between Mary and me, at least initially. As we proceeded through the frozen section consult, things seemed to thaw. Nevertheless, there was not the usual comradery between us.

That is one of the most awful things about a lawsuit—the tension it produces between physicians, and the resultant loss of teamwork and comradery. Lowell has commanded me not to talk about the lawsuit to anyone, and that certainly includes Dr. Bishop. But that means there is always a guarded tone to all of our interactions, even ones having nothing to do with the lawsuit. This lawsuit is like this big canyon that we have to tiptoe around. We can't let anything about the lawsuit slip into any conversation, lest we be asked about it in a deposition or trial. This really cuts down on relaxed and open communication. You would think it would not be that hard to refrain from talking about the lawsuit, but it is, to the point that I find myself avoiding Mary. In fact, I find myself avoiding everyone.

Bruce Palmore and Billy Swenson, the two cytotechnologists involved in the case, do not have any malpractice insurance whatsoever. I guess that's why they were not named in the suit. Lowell sent me a short note saying that our malpractice insurer, Mutual Malpractice, will be providing attorneys for Bruce and Billy.

Monday, August 11, Year 1

Today I met with the Dean of the Film School, where I will be studying screenwriting. He is not surprised that I am changing careers. "The professions are really scary these days," he said.

I will be taking these courses:

1. Writing for TV

2. Adaptations

3. Advanced Screenwriting

4. Film Production One

"You'll be busy but you'll love it," said the Dean.

I can take these relatively advanced screenwriting courses because I have already taken prerequisite, Beginning Screenwriting. The screenplay I wrote for the course, *Complications,* is one of the screenplays at Warner Brothers and MGM. I also pitched this screenplay to the Programming Director at HBO, who looked it over, along with a reader. HBO passed on it, which is fine; it's a free country and there's no law that says HBO has to option or produce my work. What is really good karma, though, is the courteous way they read it and passed on to me their comments and criticism, which I used when I converted the screenplay into a novel. Since that time, HBO has gone on a tremendously successful run producing shows like *The Sopranos, The Wire,* and *Game of Thrones,* the result of good karma.

I am looking forward to doing something creative with my right brain rather than using my analytic scientific left brain. My left brain is like a well that has run dry. There's nothing left.

My wife, Sarah, is supportive of the career change from medicine to writing. "I always thought that you would write someday," she said. "You've served your time, put off writing long enough. My only worry is that you will not have the success in writing that you have had in medicine, and that will bother you."

My three boys are fourteen, nineteen, and twenty-one years old. The two older ones are away at college, the youngest getting ready to start high school. Like most youngsters, they like stability.

I think financially we will be okay. We live a frugal life, and I have had a knack for investing. Our funds should be adequate. The joke goes: What do you need to be a writer? Answer: An independent income.

CHAPTER 10

Tuesday, August 19, Year 1

Today I met with Lowell Pound in his office. Getting there was an adventure. His office is downtown at the City Complex, which is near the county and city government buildings, as well as courthouses and law offices where Lowell can do his work—convenient for him, but not so convenient for me.

Where to park? I had difficulty finding anywhere to park. I finally made a difficult left turn into a parking garage that said "No public parking." I was able to persuade the attendant to let me park there, only under the condition that I get my parking ticket stamped by Lowell's law firm. I think he was skeptical I was a client.

Maybe it was the way I was dressed—jeans, short-sleeve cotton shirt, and denim jacket—very Hollywood chic, I thought. The men who rode up with me in the elevator wore dark suits, spotless white shirts, and conservative ties; the women were glamorous with dresses, heels, and perfect makeup. Everyone looked smarter than me.

Thick double doors (oak, I think) guarded Lowell's law offices. A wood counter, similar to those seen in college registration offices throughout the land, separated me from the receptionist wearing a black dress with nylons. A man in a suit, with a graying beard, was leaning over the counter, reading the *Dallas Morning News*. Lowell wasn't ready for me yet, so the receptionist offered me some coffee while I waited, which I took with a lot of cream and sugar—a coffee milkshake. Demure ceiling lights helped illuminate the seating choices, to my left a couch with a shaded floor lamp at one end, and straight ahead two wing chairs separated by yet another lamp. I chose one of the wing chairs so that I could look outside through floor-to-ceiling windows.

It was quite a view, what you would expect to see from the twenty-seventh floor: start with a sunny backdrop of flat fields and distant horizon, the kind of space to roam and live I saw as I drove here twenty-seven years ago to enroll at Ivory Medical School, the beautiful kind of land I never wanted to leave, where I graduated from medical school, started a family, established a practice, and put down roots. It is where I go to church. It is where I will be buried. Government buildings are across the street, with adjacent parking lots. To my right, next to some railroad tracks, a Virginia Slims sign says "It's a woman thing." Finally, in the distance past the buildings, barely visible, I saw the ubiquitous Marlboro Man riding the plains. I drank my coffee as I waited.

Lowell came to get me, and we walked down a long corridor. To my right I looked through more floor-to-ceiling windows to see a concrete patio with a few wrought-iron chairs and tables and a few interspersed small trees planted in white pots. There was a short black railing around the patio and then a drop-off of twenty-seven floors. It would be easy to open one of the doors to the outside, take a few steps, and jump. We didn't go in that direction.

Instead we turned left and opened a thick door guarding a large conference room, which dwarfed little old me. Oak furniture dominated, including a conference table about fifteen feet long, chairs, and a coffee cabinet to my right—no Naugahyde or Formica contaminated this room. To my left was an alcove with a sink and a small brown refrigerator. The lighting was gentle, but bright enough. Lowell and I sat at the end of the table closest to the door.

Our meeting got off to a slow start. Lowell thought he had returned some documents to me—our proposed answers to the plaintiff's first set of interrogatories as well as a copy of the *Cytology Procedure Manual*. I told Lowell I didn't have them, and Lowell insisted he had returned them to me. Finally Lowell left to search his office, and he returned shortly with the documents we needed. "I stand corrected," he said. "I still have them."

Lowell clearly does not like this case. As we worked together, he did a lot of frowning and shook his head a lot. He does not like the idea of our part-time cytotechnologists (Bruce Palmore and Billy Swenson) coming into our laboratory on nights and weekends and getting paid a set amount of money per slide screened. Lowell kept going on about how "bad it looked," that we "had guys coming in from other cities, from the Air Force [Billy] and other jobs [Bruce]" and how "it didn't look good."

Our defense, such as it is, is this: Between the owners of the lab—me, Reynolds, and Larry—there is close to a century of cytopathology experience, and, that it was, and is, our judgment that Billy and Bruce are good competent cytotechnologists who did, and are doing, a good job.

Lowell is afraid that we will be laughed out of court if we try to take the independent contractor defense route, i.e., claim that these two individuals are independent contractors and not employees, and therefore they should bear responsibility for their actions rather than Pathology Services, P.C. There is too much on file that rules out that approach, in Lowell's opinion.

Instead, Lowell wants our defense to be what he calls a "bolt of lightning" strategy—that what happened to Pathology Services, P.C., and the plaintiff could happen anytime, anywhere—could happen to any lab. Of course, there are two Pap smears involved, so in this metaphor there are two lightning strikes, not one, which weakens our defense.

We got a lot done. I reminded Lowell that I would be leaving Pathology Services soon, and that from now on he needed to mail things to my home, not work, and that he would need to call me at home to reach me.

"Fine," he said. "Just don't cut me off. Without you we don't have a chance of defending this case."

With me I don't think we have a chance of defending this case.

Lowell has a tough job. Every day he has to take this case, or a case similar to it, and compete against those smartly dressed men and women I noticed in the elevator, and try to win. Every day those smartly dressed, competent, intelligent men and women wake up in the morning and try to figure out ways to mess up his day with motions, depositions, trials, paperwork, games, and gimmicks to try to gain an advantage and win. It is up to Lowell to deal with that every day, to try to defend me and doctors like me for little, if any, thanks. He is dealing with doctors who are having the worst experience of their professional lives, maybe the worst experience of their lives period. Doctors are not a jovial genial happy group to begin with, and no one is having fun defending a lawsuit, especially in cases like this, where the plaintiff is certainly more sympathetic than the doctors. It's hard. Like life.

Wednesday, August 20, Year 1

Today I sent a memo to everyone at Pathology Services, P.C., announcing that I would be leaving. Officially I am announcing this as a leave of absence, but I doubt if I will be back.

Word of my resignation may have already leaked out earlier, but up to now I have communicated this only to Reynolds and Larry, and they have kept it a secret. I suspect they hoped I would change my mind; plus they have told me that my leaving will be an earthquake affecting our employees and customers. So it's kind of been a secret. That is what they wanted, and that was okay with me, because I didn't want a long lame-duck period. I have left jobs before, and I don't like that awkward interval when I am working with people, but not really involved in long-range planning, and everyone says goodbye, which is awkward, and can get emotional—and all the while I have to do as much work as ever. I am ready to go.

I sent this memo today:

"I am beginning a leave of absence September 1.

I have written a couple of screenplays, and my plan is to turn them into movies. I am going to try to make a living as a writer.

I pause here for laughter and any (possibly derisive) comments.

Yes, I am well aware that my chances for success, at least financial success, are quite small. But I am going to try.

So why am I leaving medicine and pathology, at least for a while? Simply put, I am tired of coming to work each day feeling like a target instead of a healer.

Leaving at this time is difficult, because I truly like everyone who works here. I cannot remember a time in the 15 years I have been here that we have had a more competent, cohesive group.

I wish all of you the best."

Thursday, August 21, Year 1

Tonight I went to an orientation meeting at Dallas Film School. It was held in the auditorium. Hundreds of students in their late teens and early twenties were milling about and talking loudly, cutting up, nervous.

At age forty-eight I was by far the oldest student there. Before the meeting, the Dean of the school walked over to me. "Having feelings of *déjà vu?*" he asked.

"No, but I sure am feeling younger," I said.

Friday, August 22, Year 1

Today was my last day of work at Pathology Services, P.C., a sad day but a happy day too. I worked at Pinnacle Hospital, and the hospital laboratory staff had a small, low-key farewell party for me; there was a cake, a card, and a few thoughtful gifts.

When I came home, I went to my study and stored my two microscopes and textbooks. Then I went to the garage and threw away everything else related to medicine, filling up two trash cans with slides, files, memos, procedures, old journals, presentations, anything else having to do with my professional life. It was cathartic, a relief, like shrugging my shoulders and getting the world off my back. I had no idea I was so stressed out.

Tuesday, September 2, Year 1

I am officially a film student, after my first Writing for TV class. The teacher is Charles Wilson, who, until the last few days, lived in Los Angeles. There he wrote for *Step by Step*, a television comedy about a blended family. He is tall, with dark hair, black wire-frame glasses, and quite slim and handsome, very Hollywood. He got burnt out with Hollywood and the kind of writing he was doing: "I was the only writer on staff who actually had children, and I was writing dialogue for these bratty kids, that got laughs, but if one of my kids lipped off like that, I would slap them in the face. I couldn't live with myself." His wife is good with computers and got a job with Ross Perot's company, so he and his family moved here. Then this teaching gig opened up, so it all worked out. He is quite enthusiastic and talented. I think this will be a great course.

Thursday, September 4, Year 1

There is now a change of setting for the phone calls, which will be at home. I have a study, where among other things I keep all of the records related to the lawsuit. They about fill a closet. I don't have a phone there, though, so I will be in the kitchen when I talk on the phone. It's a simple kitchen. There is a serviceable but not glamourous table where the five of us eat our meals. When we have company, we eat at a nice antique table in the dining room. The kitchen has a view out to our backyard, which is about an acre, with a lot of trees. The houses of our next-door neighbors are not really visible. Past our backyard are a gravel road and then the rolling hills of North Texas, so I'm kind of in a subdivision but also the country. It's not Southfork Ranch, but it's home. The phone is on desk next to the passageway to the TV room, so I can sit, talk, and write.

The phone rang this morning, but the caller hung up before I could answer it, only ringing twice. Caller ID identified Lowell Pound, so I returned the call. He wanted to go over the *Cytology Procedure Manual* with me and the case as a whole. "Are there any weaknesses I need to know about?" he asked.

I told him there are two:

First, it's the standard of care, and it's in our procedure manual, that when tissue is removed from the cervix, by biopsy or resection or whatever, and there have been previous Pap smears, the results of the tissue study need to be correlated with the previous Pap smear findings, and the results of that correlation documented. Our procedure manual says that this correlation is to be documented in the surgical pathology report of the tissue. That was not done. In Dr. Reynolds Price's surgical pathology report diagnosing Ms. Hawthorne's malignant tumor of the cervix, there is nary a word about the previous normal Pap smears. There should have been a comment in the report, something to the effect that the previous Pap smears were examined and the findings of the present specimen do not correlate with the results of the previous normal Pap smears, and some sort of explanation. To repeat, this was not done.

Second, if the Pap smear cytology does not correlate with tissue later removed from the patient's cervix, which was clearly the case with respect to Lynn Hawthorne's cervical biopsy, our procedure manual instructs us that the Pap smears in question need to be rescreened, to be sure there was not a mistake. That also was not done.

I have discussed this with Dr. Price, who rants and raves about it, but has no explanation for why he didn't do what he was supposed to. He should have had the results of Lynn Hawthorne's Pap smear in front of him on a computer printout when he looked at her cervical biopsy slides demonstrating cancer. He should have commented in the surgical pathology report that the previous Pap smears *did not* correlate with the findings of the cervical biopsy. Then Dr. Price, or a cytotech, or *somebody* should have rescreened the Pap smears to make sure there was not a mistake. Not for the first time, I really wish Dr. Price had done what he was supposed to do.

Lowell said that our side begins giving depositions November 4 and 5. Reynolds Price and I will meet on November 3, a Monday, in Lowell's office. The schedule is that Billy Swenson and Bruce Palmore, the cytotechnologists, will give their depositions on November 4; Reynolds and I will give our depositions November 5, me in the morning, and Reynolds in the afternoon.

In some ways this lawsuit is moving along fairly rapidly. When this thing started, I thought it would be at least a year before depositions happened, maybe longer. Here it is less than seven months since the lawsuit was filed, and Lynn Hawthorne has already given two depositions, and ours will begin soon.

Saturday, September 6, Year 1

In the mail today I received the videotape of Lynn Hawthorne's evidentiary deposition. I am in no hurry to see it.

Monday, September 8, Year 1

Today I watched the tape of Lynn Hawthorne's evidentiary deposition. Her appearance is that of a woman in shock, like one of those hurricane/earthquake/tornado survivors who have lost everything, which of course she has. She is dying, and there is no husband around to take care of her or her child. According to her testimony, her ex-husband is "not involved, and no help." She needs to prevail in this lawsuit if her daughter is to have a future.

Lowell Pound has told me that her attorney, Scott Francis, did a poor job of questioning her, that he had asked Ms. Hawthorne a lot of things that would not be admissible. I don't know about that. My experience is that there is a bias in the system that favors plaintiffs, and whatever Scott Francis thinks he needs to be admitted into evidence will be admitted into evidence.

Over and over in the deposition there were statements by Ms. Hawthorne like "I couldn't get in to see Dr. Bishop," and "Dr. Bishop couldn't see me," and, "There was a delay in seeing Dr. Bishop." When she finally got in to see her, the cervical cancer, although small, was plain to see, ready to be biopsied by Dr. Bishop for a tissue diagnosis rendered by Dr. Price at Pathology Services. Per Ms. Hawthorne's testimony, Dr. Bishop blamed the pathologists for the delay in diagnosis. So did Dr. Smith, her Ivory Hospital oncologist.

It worked. They were not sued. We were.

Tuesday, September 9, Year 1

Today I drove to Pinnacle Hospital and sold my two hundred shares of Pathology Services stock to Reynolds Price and Larry Roundtree, so I am no longer an equal partner in the company. It's all theirs. Only Larry showed up to sign the papers.

The Pathology Services employees must have been given a heads-up that I would be there, because they had a surprise farewell party for me and gave me very thoughtful gifts. One was a coffee mug with *Complications*, one of my screenplays, engraved on the side. I also received a beautiful engraved clock and a small tape recorder. The employees had obviously given a lot of thought and time into doing this for me. It moved me very much.

Saturday, September 20, Year 1

I was getting ready to go to the Southern Methodist football game today, when the mail came. There was a letter from Lowell about my deposition scheduled for November. There was also some enclosed assigned reading, two books titled *How to Prepare for a Deposition* and *The Dos and Don'ts of a Deposition*.

I'm nervous already, and it took some of the fun out of the football game.

Sunday, September 21, Year 1

Two days ago I received the transcript of the Lynn Hawthorne evidentiary deposition. I haven't read it. There's no hurry, because I already know what's in it; I've seen the tape.

Sarah read it. "You notice Lynn Hawthorne had to get married?" she asked.

"No."

"Her daughter was born seven months after the wedding."

"Interesting. Anything else?"

"Also, I don't think she would have sued you had it not been for Drs. Bishop and Smith blaming it all on the missed Pap smears."

I don't know if I am mentioning this too much, or not enough, that there is extensive finger-pointing going on in this case. Nothing new. Every time I have been sued (so far with no awards or settlements), it has been because other physicians blamed me for bad results. At least in my experience there has not been a conspiracy of silence by physicians who protect colleagues. My experience has been the opposite—that if something goes wrong, the fingers are pointed at the pathologist. Maybe because the slides hang around forever, and if anything goes wrong, someone can look at the slides and second-guess the diagnosis, something that does not happen with, say, an emergency room physician, who, when something does not work out and the patient dies, can explain that the patient came to the emergency room in shock, unconscious, near death… "So what if I gave insulin when I should have given Ringer's lactate—you had to be there, and you weren't there, and I did the best I could."

Nothing happens to the ER doctor.

Or ask a surgeon, "Why did you amputate the wrong leg?"—and the answer will be, "The patient came to me bleeding so much. There was blood on the right leg and the left leg, on all the extremities. There was blood everywhere, and the patient was bleeding to death, and I had to stop the bleeding, so I had to amputate the leg to stop the bleeding, and it turned out it was the wrong one, but you weren't there, and I did the best I could…"

Nothing happens to the surgeon.

But a pathologist misses a diagnosis on the slide, and it stays around as is, forever, for any pathologist to look at, with more history, additional special studies, clinical follow-up, and come up with a flawless diagnosis retrospectively. The reader does not have to look far for examples: exhibits A and B are Lynn Hawthorne's Pap smears.

Dr. Bishop, who didn't get around to seeing the patient until it was too late, is not blameless in my opinion. She has not been sued.

I am not sure at this point that Dr. Smith has done anything wrong. The operations she has done should have worked, but they did not work, and her patient is dying, but that may not have been her fault. At any rate, she has not been sued.

Only the pathologists have been sued. As far as Lynn Hawthorne is concerned, it's all our fault.

Chapter 11

Monday, September 29, Year 1

I'm catching up the diary from over the weekend, when I did not get much sleep. My twenty-year-old middle son and I went to the SMU/Ole Miss football game in Oxford, Mississippi. Then Sunday morning I had to get up early to help out on a film shoot.

The game started at 11 a.m. and ended about 3 p.m. We left after the game and got home about 2 a.m. Before I went to bed, I checked my mail, and at the top of the stack was a letter from Lowell marked "Personal and Confidential." Every time I get one of these letters, I get queasy and my heart starts racing. These letters are never good news, and it seems the lawsuit never takes a rest. The letter was about a third set of interrogatories from the plaintiff, primarily requests for "Employment Records" for Billy Swenson and Bruce Palmore, more work for me, but no big deal. Still, I had trouble falling asleep.

At 5 a.m. Sunday I was working as an electrician/gofer on a full-length film written, produced, and directed by a local attorney/film student, about my age, who is in one of my screenwriting classes, who is having a midlife crisis same as me. He is taking a leave of absence from his very successful law practice (he is always on the Best Lawyers lists) to produce and direct his film, a comedy/adventure about a teenage girl who faces teenage challenges of fitting in, and the unorthodox lengths she goes to improve her situation. We filmed at a local restaurant, and we had to shoot the scenes early on a Sunday morning so we wouldn't interfere with the business of this very chic North Dallas restaurant. The climactic scene was in the kitchen, where the heroine is "helping out" in the kitchen when she inadvertently throws a big squid (calamari) in the face of the owner/chef; the actor playing the role really is the owner/chef of the restaurant. The scene was funny and well done. We then moved to other locations, and I didn't get home till after dark, where I collapsed.

While in Oxford, I visited William Faulkner's house. I've also been to Ernest Hemingway's house in Key West, Florida. Their ghosts seem to inhabit these places; at any rate, I feel the presence of these great writers.

My pencil seems to weep whenever I read their works. I read Faulkner's short story *Barn Burning* and it is so good. Oh, for a Muse like that. Well, we can't all be Faulkner or Hemingway or Shakespeare. This work will not be the brightest star in the sky, but I hope it contributes a little light.

I was talking to Reynolds about how great *Barn Burning* is, and Faulkner, and he agreed but asked, "If William Faulkner were alive today, would anyone publish him, and would anyone read him?"

Probably not.

Wednesday, October 8, Year 1

Last night I got home about 10 p.m. from my Adaptations class. Another letter from Lowell was waiting. In it he related that he had given Scott Francis some answers to the plaintiff's interrogatories. Lowell also says that he is not going to make a motion to dismiss the case on the grounds that Billy Swenson and Bruce Palmore are independent contractor cytotechnologists and therefore not our employees or agents. He thinks we "would lose such a motion and impair our credibility with the court."

The coursework for the Adaptions class is demanding. Every week a work of art is assigned, usually a book like *A River Runs through It*. Our assignment for the week is to read the book and answer a long worksheet with many questions: who is the protagonist, who is the antagonist, who is the mentor, what is the hero's journey, what are the challenges in adapting this work to the screen, how would you overcome them?—question after question. The answers are to be written. Then the assignment is to read the screenplay and answer the same questions, again in writing. After all that, the assignment is to watch the film and answer how the director handled these challenges, and how the director's version differed from the screenplay. The assignments involve a lot of writing; after all this is a writing class. During class all of these issues are discussed. Another week and the process is repeated with different source material. In addition, before the course is finished, I have to find a book or other source material to adapt, and write out how I would go about adapting it. My choice is one of Walker Percy's books.

Let's take this approach to *Diary of a Lawsuit: A Physician's Journey and Survival Guide*.

Overview.

What is the genre and style or approach? This is a realistic docudrama. Pap smear litigation is a real event, a crisis actually, involving numerous pathologists.

Place and time.

Where? Dallas, Texas.

When? Present day.

What are the historical contexts? There is a shortage of physicians, which is getting worse. A person goes into medicine, mainly to help people, to make a living, sure, even a good living, but gets sidetracked by competing extrinsic factors—dealing with insurance companies, hospital businessmen, and, as this story describes, attorneys. Word gets around, and the field of medicine does not have near the cachet and desirability it did when I was in medical school; this is one reason for the shortage of physicians all of us are struggling with. I have read that 50% of physicians are suffering from burnout. My experience is that this is a low estimate. Almost every physician I know is suffering from burnout.

Characters and Driving Desires.

Protagonist: Me, Jack Spenser. I want this lawsuit to be over with so that I can get on with what I regard as my purpose in life, which is, paraphrasing Aristotle, to find out what my function in life is and perform that function to the best of my ability, to try to make the world a better place. That is what I tried to do when I was practicing pathology. Therefore this lawsuit is like a stake directed at my purpose, my function, my heart, and my soul. My driving desire is to survive and find out what I am to do with the rest of my life, and write.

Instigator: Lynn Hawthorne. She wants to provide the needed resources for her daughter, hopefully before she dies—an understandable, admirable goal.

Antagonist: Scott Francis. My perception is that his driving desire in this narrative is to help Lynn Hawthorne and also collect a fee and/or part of the settlement. He is not doing this *pro bono*.

Friends: Wife and family.

Allies: Reynolds Price and Larry Roundtree.

Mentor/Guide: Lowell Pound.

Structure.

Point of view: The story is told from my point of view. I am trying to be a reliable narrator, recognizing that there is no such thing as a reliable narrator.

Where does it begin and end: The story began with the lawsuit. It will end when it feels right.

Theme.

There are no guarantees in life. One can follow the rules, work hard, do the right thing—but not avoid bad times and conflict. Ms. Hawthorne did nothing wrong, and she is dying, will die soon. She did nothing wrong and will die at a young age, leaving behind an orphan daughter. Really no need to expand on this—it's about as bad as it gets.

In my case I have always tried to do the right thing and obey the rules—studied hard in college to get grades good enough to get in Ivory Med School and then completed a demanding residency where I learned my pathology craft. In private practice, every day I came to work and did my best. I have had some success. I have about half a dozen published scientific/medical articles in peer-reviewed journals. I was on the Board at Pinnacle Hospital, an honor, one of four physicians out of a medical staff of a few hundred, voted in by my physician peers. I was on the Board of the American Red Cross, and the Chairman the Medical Advisory Committee.

At church I taught fifth-grade Sunday school for about eight years. I served terms as Chairman of the Staff Parish Committee and Chairman of the Administrative Board.

I thought I was a respected member of the community, including the medical community, where I thought I was regarded as a good physician and pathologist by my peers, a man of integrity and competence, a leader. I thought my good deeds would be talismans to protect me from harm.

That didn't happen. The lawsuit says in so many words that I am a sorry pathologist working at a sorry lab. With respect to the Pap smears, a number of pathologists *retrospectively* have said we blew it. A colleague and classmate, Dr. Benedict Harris, finds perfectly credible the lies that have been told to him by one of his cytotechnologists, and spreads those lies to anyone who will listen, including my peers at Medical Malpractice and my attorney. Two of my ob-gyn colleagues and two radiologists at Pinnacle have pointed their fingers at me and my lab, blaming us for the tragic things that have happened to Ms. Hawthorne. There is more of that to come, I suspect.

The theme is that one is never safe. There are no guarantees in this world. I am hanging on by my fingernails, same as everyone else.

Thursday, October 9, Year 1

I came home this evening around 8 p.m., after editing my Film Production One project for several hours. I wrote a short screenplay, shot the scenes, and now I am trying to put it together as a short film.

A letter from Lowell was waiting. It was a copy of a communication from Scott Francis to Lowell Pound describing a conversation between the two of them about settling this lawsuit. It looks like Mr. Francis wants to do his depositions of our side and then settle.

Wednesday, October 15, Year 1

Reynolds phoned me at home a couple of times. The first time he asked me, "Have you talked to Lowell about his latest letter, the one about settling the case?"

"No. I've seen the letter, but I haven't talked to him about it."

"I'll call him. Anything you want me to say vis-à-vis a settlement?"

"My attitude is the same as it's been for a long time. I would settle this case for a million dollars or less, in the name of Pathology Services, P.C., not me personally. Two of the worst parts of any lawsuit are the deposition and the trial. I would prefer to settle the case before my deposition. After the deposition, my inclination to settle will probably go down."

Reynolds also asked me to find some documents from the Federal Register about Pap smear regulations. He had left his copies on a plane. It took a while, but I finally found the documents Reynolds needs.

Then Reynolds called again. I picked up the phone. "I didn't mean to call you," he said.

"Since you did, what did you find out?"

"Lowell is not going to answer Francis's letter. Lowell thinks Francis is a 'real asshole.'"

"I would think Lynn Hawthorne should be willing to settle. One million dollars now, before she dies, in my opinion, is worth more than ten times that much after she dies, when her convict ex-husband can try to get his grubby hands on it."

"Well, the way I figure it, sooner or later Francis has an obligation to tell his client that the defendants are willing to settle, and that this is a very defensible case, in my opinion. The Federal Register says that false negatives can run up to 30%. We can get hundreds of pathologists to testify for us. To me it's like Lynn Hawthorne was struck by lightning— only in this case there are a few pathologists (us) standing nearby to take the financial hit."

Tuesday, October 21, Year 1

We finally caught a break, a huge break! I received the report from the staff at the Medical University of South Carolina, the ones who did a blind review of the two infamous Pap smears that this lawsuit is about. Here is a summary of their report:

With respect to the earlier slide, eight out of ten supervisor level cytotechnologists saw nothing abnormal on the slide—the same report our lab rendered! Two saw atypical cells of "Undetermined Significance" and **may not be representative of a definitive abnormality** (their boldface).

With respect to the second later Pap smear, six out of ten supervisor cytotechnologists called it "Within Normal Limits," which is to say they saw no abnormal cells, again the same report our laboratory rendered! Two saw atypical cells of "Undetermined Significance" and two rendered diagnoses of "Low Grade" lesions.

None of the supervisor level cytotechnologists saw anything in either Pap smear approaching a malignant diagnosis. I feel vindicated.

"Aren't you sad you quit?" said my twenty-one-year-old son.

Wednesday, October 22, Year 1

I got another letter from Lowell today. They seem to come daily. Today's letter described the legal posturing and maneuvering going on about a hearing to have the case against us dismissed. My humble opinion: we don't have a snowball's chance in hell of getting this case dismissed.

Still, the South Carolina people really helped our defense. A blind review like they did is the only way to get a fair reading of the Pap smears. If Lowell or Scott Francis takes the Pap smears to someone for a second opinion, red flags go up all over the place. Any reviewer will think: Why am I being asked to look at these slides? They can't be normal.

I have been trying to think of a metaphor that will make sense to a jury, about how slides viewed in retrospect can have cells easily identified that are almost impossible to recognize during the initial examination. Here is what I came up with:

Suppose you are traveling down a street or highway looking for a particular turn. You may look quite carefully, but still miss it. You may blink your eye, misread a sign, not see a poorly illuminated sign, it's raining—any number of reasons. When you go too far, you turn around and look again for the street you missed. The second time you may very well see the turn you missed earlier. Or, if you miss it again and turn around, you may see the road you missed the first two times.

Looking at a Pap smear is like that. You can be very careful and still miss the abnormal cells. However, if you know there have to be abnormal cells there (because the patient now has cervical cancer), you can look and look until you find abnormal cells, which is not that hard to do, because there are two hundred to three hundred thousand cells on a Pap smear to look at, and sooner or later you can find something, malignant cell or not, to match up with the malignancy present in the patient. However, it is totally impractical to look at every Pap smear like this; you'd never have a normal Pap smear. It would be a useless test.

I had my Advanced Screenwriting Class today. The teacher is another transplant from Los Angeles, where he was making a living as a cinematographer, but what he really wants to do is write and teach. So he is on the faculty here, teaching Advanced Screenwriting, as well as teaching my Film Production One class. He loves to teach. Instead of saying like most: "Those who can, do, and those who can't, teach," he says, "Those who can't teach, don't teach." His brother is a physician, an emergency room physician. Like me, his brother is burned out, and likes films, and my teacher tells me, "My brother says the same things you do, hates medicine and loves films. I think he will be leaving medicine soon, to make movies."

One of the best parts of the Advanced Screenwriting Class is the assigned films and screenplays:

Spike Lee's *She's Got to Have It*, a comedy and character study.

The Coen brothers' *Barton Fink*, an exploration of the artistic creative process, done in the typical Coen brothers' violent fashion.

Alfred Hitchcock's *Psycho*. What does an audience do when the protagonist is stabbed to death in the shower, who do you identify with, what do you do?

Rob Reiner's *This is Spinal Tap*, the hilarious parody of a documentary.

Hilary Henkin's *Romeo is Bleeding*—got to "feed the hole" a metaphor for striving and trying to build up tangible treasures at the expense of spiritual ones.

Jon Jost's *All the Vermeers in New York*. I never heard of Vermeer's art until I saw the film. Now he is one of my favorite artists, and prints of his paintings are prominent in my house, demonstrating what he can do with light.

Richard Linklater's *Dazed and Confused*, the description of high school coming of age that all of us experience one way or another, filmed with flat simple cinematography.

Christopher McQuarrie's *The Usual Suspects*. My test for any person who claims to be a "film buff" is have you seen *The Usual Suspects*? A "yes" answer, and I regard the person as probably a true film buff. A "no" answer, and I am skeptical that this person is a true film buff.

Martin Scorsese's *After Hours*, a retelling of *The Wizard of Oz*, in a New York City setting, done in a hilarious fashion.

Woody Allen's *Crimes and Misdemeanors*, his best and deepest film.

Thursday, October 23, Year 1

My daily letter from Lowell was in the mail, reminding me that I have a meeting with him a week from Monday to get ready for my deposition, and that the depositions of Billy Swenson and Bruce Palmore, our cytotechnologists, will be the following day, Tuesday, followed by depositions of Reynolds and me on the next day, Wednesday. Quite a week, which Lowell realizes, stating, "That a meeting on Monday afternoon and depositions on Tuesday and Wednesday might be problematic for your work schedules… nevertheless… I think you should try, if at all possible, to be present for the depositions of Swenson and Palmore and for each other's depositions."

I wouldn't miss it for the world.

Saturday, October 25, Year 1

Reynolds called. He wants the three owners of Pathology Services at the time of the Pap smears—Larry Roundtree, Reynolds, and myself—to get together before the depositions. That way we will be prepared. Good idea. We decided to meet Tuesday morning.

Sunday, October 26, Year 1

No day of rest for those who have been sued. To prepare for our meeting on Tuesday, I decided to organize my files having to do with this lawsuit. Quite a task. This lawsuit has generated enough paperwork to literally fill the closet in my study, three large suitcases, and the lawsuit has barely begun.

Tuesday, October 28, Year 1

I met with Reynolds and Larry today. We went over the CLIA (Clinical Laboratory Improvement Act) regulations line by line to make sure we were in compliance. After reviewing seventy-three pages of regulations, the only two shortcomings are the ones I have already pointed out to Lowell:

1. According to the regs, surgical pathology cases (e.g., the cervical biopsy examined in our lab that Reynolds diagnosed as

malignant) are to be correlated with any Pap smears done within the past year. Reynolds did not do that, even though it is in the regulations and our procedure manual to do so. Reynolds does not know why he didn't do this.

2. According to the regs and our procedure manual, Pap smears that don't correlate with the biopsy or follow-up tissue are to be re-screened. That wasn't done either, by Reynolds or anybody else.

Otherwise, I think we are in good shape and can document that we did everything we were supposed to do. Reynolds emphasizes that there are three points to get across in our depositions:

1. We think the Pap smear slides are negative, with no abnormal cells, and our Pap smear reports are accurate.

2. We have complied with all applicable regulations, the two short-comings described above notwithstanding. In fact, we passed with flying colors all inspections, including inspections by the state and the College of American Pathologists.

3. In *any* laboratory that does Pap smears, there is a false negative rate of up to 30%.

4. Friday, October 31, Year 1

I received yet another letter from Lowell today. He has talked to Dr. Smith, the gynecologic oncologist at Ivory Medical Center who took care of Lynn Hawthorne, the one who did everything in her power to make sure we were blamed for the unfortunate results of the surgery she performed.

Interestingly, now Dr. Smith says she does not want to be an advocate for either side, the plaintiff or the defendants. So after giving Lynn Hawthorne the gun to point at us, saying all her problems are because we messed up her Pap smears, getting us named in a lawsuit, Dr. Smith wants to wash her hands of the whole thing.

Dr. Smith has a lot of sympathy for both sides, she says. In particular, Dr. Smith doesn't understand why Ms. Hawthorne is doing so poorly after the surgery she did. Even after what she calls our "misses," Dr. Smith felt Ms. Hawthorne had a good prognosis when she came to

Ivory—"93% of the patients who come to Ivory in her condition are cancer-free at five years after treatment, and are essentially cured." That Lynn Hawthorne had such a bad outcome, with a recurrence of the cancer five months after the initial operation, mystifies Dr. Smith. "Either she has a highly unusual form of cancer, or her immune system is quiet weak."

Here's another possibility: you messed up the operation and treatment and shifted the blame to us.

Lowell mentioned the South Carolina study, which exonerates us. Dr. Smith conceded that this was a good way to defend the case, but she "does not want to get dragged into the middle of this lawsuit."

Thanks for nothing.

I can believe Dr. Smith does not want to get involved. She does not want anyone looking over her shoulder and second-guessing her. Dr. Smith wants us to be second-guessed, and she made sure that we were.

Dr. Smith was one of my teachers when I was a medical student at Ivory Medical School. I thought she was an overrated pompous jerk then. I still do.

CHAPTER 12

Monday, November 3, Year 1

I met with Lowell Pound and Reynolds Price this afternoon at Lowell's office in the City Complex. Once again I rode the elevator to the twenty-seventh floor, and once again those who got on and off the elevator were better looking and better dressed than me, probably smarter too. I was scared.

Lowell didn't make me feel better. Lowell began by asking me a few sample questions, which he knows Scott Francis likes to ask, so I will be prepared for the deposition in less than forty-eight hours. Reynolds listened. It went like this:

"Dr. Spenser, did you meet the standard of care with respect to Lynn Hawthorne's Pap smears?"

"Yes."

"What is the standard of care with regard to Pap smears?"

"Um, er, uh…"

Lowell asked Reynolds some similar questions. His answers were better than mine.

"We can live with your answers," Lowell said to Reynolds. Lowell turned to me. "We cannot live with your answers."

The answers I should have given go like this. The standard of care is a duty that is imposed on everyone, to exercise ordinary care in what one does. Negligence is a failure to do what is reasonably prudent under the circumstances. My answer to Lowell should have been "I did, and our laboratory did, what was reasonable and prudent with respect to the examination of Lynn Hawthorne's Pap smears." Our safety net for this: we passed regular inspections by licensing and accrediting agencies, which found what we were doing acceptable.

There was a lot more advice like "don't talk too much, watch for trick questions, don't volunteer information..."—kind of common sense and boring. We moved on.

"Can we make anything of this lady's sexual history that may have caused her cancer?" asked Lowell.

"Yes!" said Reynolds. "In the first surgical pathology report from Ivory, they diagnosed condylomatous changes, a sexually transmitted disease by human papillomavirus."

Lowell looked at me. I nodded. "He's right."

Lowell isn't sure whether we can use this for our defense or not. It was time to wrap things up.

"Finally," Lowell said, "and I am looking at you, Reynolds, as I say this, don't lose your temper."

"That's not going to happen," I said. "Reynolds didn't last for over twenty years in private practice by losing his temper at the wrong time. He will be fine."

Tuesday, November 4, Year 1

Billy Swenson and Bruce Palmore, our cytotechnologists, gave their depositions today, which took place in a conference room of their attorney, Everton Hawkins. Bruce, Billy, Reynolds, Mr. Hawkins, Lowell, and I were in the conference room, waiting for Scott Francis. There was an article in the Sunday paper that said Scott Francis was being considered as an appointee to be a judge, so when Scott Francis finally showed up, Lowell said, "All rise." Everyone laughed.

Billy's deposition was in the morning. He is a short, slim, lean man, with blond hair, and glasses that give him a scholarly but meek look, like an insecure young accountant. He is in his late twenties. After about an hour of questioning, Scott Francis looked at Bruce Palmore sitting across from him, as if he had just noticed him. Francis wanted Bruce to leave while Billy was questioned. Everton Hawkins put up some resistance to this. They decided to take a break and look up some rulings. When we came back from the break, Bruce was gone.

Billy did a pretty good job. I was pleased, because going into the depositions, I thought he was the weaker of our two cytotechnologists. I was glad to get that deposition out of the way, and I was confident

Bruce's deposition in the afternoon would go well. Nothing to worry about.

Well, my grandmother always said, "It's not what you worry about that gets you. It's what you don't worry about that gets you."

Wise woman, because Bruce's deposition did not go well and worried the hell out of me. Like Billy, Bruce is in his late twenties and is a relatively short man, about five feet five or so. Bruce has dark hair behind a receding hairline. Unlike Billy, Bruce stumbled, stammered, and equivocated during his deposition. He kept talking about Ms. Hawthorne's Pap smears being "suboptimal," which sure didn't help our cause. What really puzzled me was that Bruce didn't even use the word "suboptimal" on his screening worksheet report or anywhere else.

For a while Scott Francis was worried he would not finish the depositions today. His son had a Cub Scout pack meeting, and Mr. Francis felt he had to be there—he couldn't work late. The depositions ended a little after 4 p.m. It was a long day.

It wasn't over. Lowell, Reynolds, and I walked to Lowell's office to prepare for tomorrow's depositions, when Reynolds and I will be questioned. I had an Adaptations class at 5:30 p.m., so I had to leave early, much to Reynolds's dismay. "This is my new life," I said. We agreed to meet tomorrow morning at 7 a.m. to finish our preparations before the depositions starting at 8 a.m.

Some very strange things have been happening in Adaptations class, which is irritating, but I should have been ready for it. I have a friend at church, who is a very talented songwriter, talented enough to be nominated for a Grammy award. He has been very supportive of my writing and kind of supportive of my going to film school, but he is not sure creative art like writing can be taught. Also, he warned me, "Sooner or later you are going to run into a teacher who does not have your gift, and he will be jealous and will try to destroy you."

Well, it's kind of happening in my Adaptations class. We were discussing log lines, which are one-line summaries of a film, and how to write them. The movie *Tootsie* came up for discussion. I asked the teacher for an example of a log line to use for *Tootsie*. He hemmed and hawed and said something like, "Well, I would need some time to consider…"

Without thinking further, I immediately said, "By becoming a woman, he became more of a man."

Dead silence. I nailed it.

Well, one of the assigned source materials for our course is to adapt the Supreme Court decision *Roe versus Wade* about abortion, which was covered in the movie *Citizen Ruth*. I completed the assignment and got scathing written criticisms, including "You let your personal views of abortion affect your writing."

This criticism is wrong and out of line, because the teacher has no idea what my views on abortion are. I'm glad my songwriter friend gave me some warning.

Wednesday, November 5, Year 1

I gave my deposition this morning, a very draining experience—a series of seemingly unending questions. I feel like someone opened a spigot and drained out everything I know about Pap smears, Pathology Services, and Lynn Hawthorne. As I write this diary entry, I am exhausted with low grade aches and pains.

The day got off to a horrible start. I arrived at Lowell's Law Offices a little before 7 a.m., as Lowell had requested, to finish preparations for the depositions. The receptionist said that Lowell hadn't arrived yet, so she escorted me to a waiting area, a sparsely furnished room with a small table and some chairs, where Reynolds was already seated. We started going over our notes, scientific articles, and records to prepare for our deposition, while we waited for Lowell. And waited. And waited. "Is Mr. Pound here yet?" we asked the receptionist from time to time, and we were repeatedly told that he hadn't arrived.

Finally, at 8 a.m., Lowell walked into the waiting room, frantic. "Where have you guys been?" he asked. "Caught in interstate traffic?"

We answered that we had been waiting for him for over an hour. Lowell said he had arrived at 7 a.m., as promised, but it evidently was beyond the competence of the receptionist to get us all together. Lowell ran off, trying to figure out who in his firm had messed up and not taken us back to Lowell's office, where he had been frantically waiting for us!

I tell this story because of Lowell's double standard regarding us. On our side Lowell expects us to be perfect, and he comes down hard on us for any shortcomings we may have—documentation that is not perfect, our cytotechnologists are not employees but independent contractors, the list of pathologists who have disagreed with our Pap smear diagnoses, the disparaging comments by Ms. Arnold—putting us down every chance he gets in a very judgmental way. But on Lowell's side, his law office is so incompetent that his receptionist can't even do her simple job of getting the three of us together. This isn't the first screw-up by him and his office. And Lowell has the nerve to lecture us! Look, I get it. Lowell has to be a realist and defend us, and he has to know our short-comings—that's part of his job. But under the circumstances and the double standard, his sanctimonious tone really gets old.

Of course, now that it was 8 a.m., Scott Francis had arrived, ready to go. So, no time for last minute preparation for my deposition. Time to get it on.

There were five of us in the conference room: Scott Francis, Lowell, Reynolds Price, the court stenographer, and me. The men were in suits, the court stenographer in a dress. We all looked sharp.

Mr. Francis asked the questions in a soft voice, and as I answered them, he was in perpetual motion, even though he remained sitting. He wrinkled his forehead, opened his eyes wide, then closed them, nodded his head up and down, and furrowed his eyebrows. His feet tapped the floor and his legs bounced up and down almost constantly. He put his knees together and then spread them apart. He rolled his pen in his hands. Sometimes he flipped through his yellow legal pad, looking for more questions, always more questions. When I answered, he leaned forward and listened so intently that I thought I must be the most interesting person on God's green earth, and for that moment, to him, I was.

My deposition took the entire morning, and Reynolds Price listened to it. Reynolds's deposition took all afternoon, and I listened to the whole thing.

Scott Francis's most effective tactic was to ask a lot of questions, many of them irrelevant, some of them personal (e.g., Q. "Do y'all attend church?" A. "Yes, sir." Q. "Where do you attend church?" A. "We go to Sinai United Methodist Church." Q. "Where is that?"…). The questions went on and on to the point of fatigue, and there was a temptation to let down my guard. Then, near the end of the deposition, when the really critical, tough questions come, he wanted me tired. This kind of questioning drove Lowell nuts, and he thinks Scott Francis is incompetent, taking all day to do what a good lawyer could do in less time.

I disagree. I think Mr. Francis's method is slow but effective. It's like a professional poker player who plays with amateurs. As the game goes on into the night, the amateurs who have day jobs get tired, and the professional still keeps going strong and makes his money.

Lowell is not impressed with my high regard for Mr. Francis. "If you think Francis is smart, I can tell you there are some guys I know who would see discrepancies and jump all over you."

"I didn't say he was smart," I said. "I said he was effective."

Strangely, once the depositions and meetings started, my feelings of intimidation and inadequacy evaporated and went away. I concentrated on what was going on, and what was being asked.

Many of the questions, of course, were about Pap smears, quality control, quality assurance, Ms. Hawthorne's medical records, our laboratory records—a lot of scientific and medical issues.

The only question that threw me off for a while was when Francis asked me questions about our procedure for what Pap smears were to be reviewed by a pathologist in addition to a cytotechnologist. I needed to demonstrate that we had such a procedure in our procedure manual, and for the life of me, I could not find it. I knew we had such a procedure, and in fact followed that procedure, I just could not find it as the minutes ticked away. After what seemed to me like an interminable length of time, I finally found the pertinent document.

Scott Francis and I do not get along. As I've mentioned, he had deposed me before for another case when I was not a defendant, but an expert witness. During that deposition, he got so exasperated with me that he turned to the opposing attorney to ask him to explain to me the purpose of a deposition.

Similarly, today at one point Mr. Francis did not like some of my answers and asked in an aggressive manner, "Was there something funny?"

"No, sir," I answered. "No."

I think I held my own. Also, I told the truth.

"I don't think I said or did anything that will sink our boat," I said to Reynolds and Lowell when it was over. They agreed.

Reynolds's deposition went well also, I thought. Of note, there were questions that put on the record that not only is he board certified in anatomic and clinical pathology, but cytopathology as well. He is a real expert in Pap smears. Most of the deposition covered the same ground as mine in the morning.

After the depositions were over, Reynolds, Lowell, and I went into Lowell's office to talk. Lowell does not think there is much chance for a reasonable settlement in this case. It's sad, tragic. Our understanding is that Lynn Hawthorne is now in the hospital with bone metastases and will die soon, and the other side is not ready to settle. Our offer to settle for a million dollars is still on the table.

I said, "Lynn Hawthorne is a lady who I think would be more interested in taking a million dollars now, before she dies, than, say, three million dollars after she dies."

"This is the reason that most people are not satisfied with the justice they get in the courts," said Lowell. "People come to the justice system thinking that there is going to be this big jackpot, and instead of settling for some reasonable amount, they mess it up. Take this case: I can tell from his questions that Francis hasn't got a clue about what he is going to get into once he learns about false negative Pap smears. But he spends his time going after you doctors, who did nothing wrong, just ticking you off."

"You got that right," I said.

"It's a breakdown in the system that these guys, the plaintiffs' attorneys, do not do the right thing and do their job. Very frustrating."

When the legal stuff was over, I went to my Advanced Screenwriting class, and I didn't get home until about 10 p.m. Reynolds had left me a message to call no matter how late, so I did.

He was panic stricken because he thought he may have perjured himself, answering some question about Billy Swenson.

"I don't remember the exact wording of the question you are worried about," I said, "but I listened to all your answers, and no alarm bells went off. In fact, I don't remember groaning, shaking, or quivering about any of your answers. You did fine."

A strange episode that tells me that this lawsuit has really hit him hard. Reynolds is about ten years older than I am, and I have kind of regarded him as a mentor, a very strong person, one who has all the answers. This lawsuit must have really shaken him to his core to make him panic over a deposition.

Friday, November 7, Year 1

I received a copy of a letter Lowell had sent to Milton Jackson, the attorney for Mutual Malpractice. In it he said the depositions of Reynolds and me had gone well.

I am relieved to have my deposition over with. I didn't realize how much it had been weighing on me, and how much I had been dreading it. I can take a deep breath.

CHAPTER 13

Wednesday, November 12, Year 1

I received two letters from Lowell Pound today, updating me on the case. The news is that Dr. Larry Roundtree and Dr. John Pelton will be giving their depositions December 16 and 17.

I'm confused. My understanding from Lowell was that Reynolds and I would give depositions, supposedly because we were "the only ones who knew what was going on" (Lowell's words not mine), and Billy Swenson and Bruce Palmore gave depositions because they were the ones who had actually looked at the Pap smears—and that would be it. But no, there's more.

My first rule of lawsuits: nobody knows anything.

When do we get to depose the plaintiff's experts? At this point, we don't even know who they are.

Friday, November 14, Year 1

Today I received another letter from Lowell. Larry and John will give their depositions on December 23 instead of December 16 and 17.

I can't get over what I regard as irresponsible behavior by Scott Francis. I think he is wasting everyone's time. We are perfectly willing to settle the case for $1 million, now. I continue to think Lynn Hawthorne would be much better off with $1 million now, which she can keep when she is alive. That way she can take steps to keep the money away from her drug addict, ex-con ex-husband. She may, or may not, get a bigger payoff after she is dead, but what are the chances that her ex-husband will then try to get custody of his daughter, and the money. I would say pretty good.

I wonder how culpable the plaintiff, Lynn Hawthorne, in all of this is. Is she demanding to be told of our settlement offers, and if so, is she refusing them?

At any rate, I wonder at the wisdom of refusing our settlement offers. As time goes on, I think our case strengthens. I don't think for a moment that we could win a jury trial, but I think the truth about Pap smears is becoming more generally known and that the public understands that false negative Pap smears are unavoidable (which we can conclusively prove with the results of the South Carolina blind review study). We would not win, but I think the jury might be inclined to give us at least some of a break in the amount of the reward. I think it is in the plaintiff's best interest to settle now.

Saturday, November 15, Year 1

I received another pile of documents from Lowell today. One was a copy of a notice of deposition and subpoena for Dr. Mary Bishop, Lynn Hawthorne's gynecologist, who sent the Pap smears and cervical biopsy to our lab from her office. Evidently Dr. Bishop has been totally uncooperative with Lowell, refusing to turn over any medical records to Lowell, even refusing to talk to Lowell. I am surprised.

Look, I don't expect her to have our back or lie for us or engage in a cover-up. I am fine if she is neutral, but she's not. None of our colleagues involved in this incident are neutral, but are supporting the other side. Dr. Bishop and Dr. Smith at Ivory felt obligated to point their fingers at us about the Pap smears, and Dr. Smith went so far as to help the other side by turning over our Pap smears to the plaintiff's attorneys, without asking us or notifying us.

It has come to this, that to get the medical records from Dr. Bishop, which we are entitled to for our defense, our lawyer has had to resort to a deposition and subpoena. Before this lawsuit I regarded her as not only a colleague, but a friend. We had a lot in common. We were both in private practice. We played softball together and had a lot of good times. We're no longer colleagues and, as far as I'm concerned, no longer friends.

Other news: the plaintiff has offered to settle the case for $1.9 million.

Lowell suggests a counteroffer of $150,000. I thought we already had an offer on the table for $1 million, but what do I know? Again, my first rule of lawsuits is that no one knows anything.

In the meantime, the interrogatories from the plaintiff keep coming. Francis sent another stack, which Lowell forwarded to me to work on, more piles and piles of paper reminds me of Dickens's *Bleak House*.

I think this lawsuit will settle in the $1 million range, the sooner the better.

Tuesday, November 18, Year 1

I received two more letters from Lowell today. One confirmed the date of December 23 as the deposition date for John Pelton and Larry Roundtree.

The other letter contained copies of Dr. Bishop's medical records of Lynn Hawthorne, which Lowell had to subpoena to get. In the records there is an interesting communication from Dr. Smith, the gynecologist/oncologist at Ivory. The gist of the communication is that Dr. Smith was troubled by the fact that the cancer was not picked up by the yearly Pap smears Lynn Hawthorne had been getting, and that Ivory had just received a new instrument in their laboratory, a "Pap Net" screening station, and that she was interested in looking at Ms. Hawthorne's Pap smear using this instrument "from an investigational standpoint at this time."

I wonder what the results of her "investigation" were. They probably would have helped our side, because I haven't heard a peep.

Monday, November 24, Year 1

Reynolds phoned me first thing this morning. He has been out of town and is now catching up with his mail. We went over our answers to the plaintiff's latest interrogatories. I had already mailed my answers to Lowell.

Reynolds is worried about John Pelton's deposition scheduled for December 23. Reynolds thinks that he is the weak link in our defense, such as it is—that John is so "arrogant" that there is no predicting how he will answer Scott Francis's questions. I agree.

Reynolds also has some slides he wants me to look at under the microscope, slides of the tissues removed during Lynn Hawthorne's operation at Ivory.

"I would love to find something Ivory missed," I said, "say a metastasis in one of the lymph nodes, which would have changed everything."

"So would I," said Reynolds.

Even so, I'm not in a hurry to look at the slides. I haven't looked through a microscope in three months. I left medicine three months ago, and I'm not anxious to go back.

Wednesday, November 26, Year 1

I received two envelopes from Lowell Pound today. He sure prefers letters to phone calls.

One envelope contained a copy of a letter to Dr. Ted Gable, thanking him for agreeing to review the Pap smears of this case. Hopefully this world expert in Pap smears can aid our defense.

The second envelope contained a copy of a letter to an economics professor at Ivory. He will examine Ms. Hawthorne's depositions, tax returns, and other documents to calculate the damages she would be entitled to recover if we are found liable—not very cheerful stuff. Lowell wants an answer by February 1.

Friday, November 28, Year 1

This afternoon Sarah and I were on our way out the door for a weekend getaway at the Turtle Creek Mansion when the mail came. In it was a packet from Lowell containing a transcript of my deposition for me to proofread. What to do? Two options:

1. Leave it at home and look at it when we return home Sunday afternoon. The downside is that then it will be hanging over me all weekend.

2. Take it along and take some time to read it in the hotel. The downside is that kind of defeats the purpose of the trip, which is to get away from cares and concerns for a weekend.

I chose option 2.

We had dinner at the hotel restaurant, one of the best meals I've ever had. The lounge just outside the restaurant had a very talented pianist/singer with a beautiful tenor voice, who sang Christmas songs. We listened for over an hour, then went up to our suite. While Sarah took a bath in the bathroom next to the bedroom, I went to the sitting room with a sofa, chairs, and table and started reading the deposition carefully, to make sure there weren't any errors. I couldn't stop reading. It took over an hour to finish it. By that time Sarah had finished her bath, gone to bed, and fallen asleep.

Sunday, November 30, Year 1

Sarah read my deposition today. I asked her how I did. She shrugged and said, "All you can do is tell the truth."

"There are all kinds of ways to tell the truth," I said.

I can live with my answers. They are the truth as I see it.

Wednesday, December 3, Year 1

Last night I was up until 4 a.m. writing. At 10:15 this morning, Reynolds woke me up with a phone call. Reynolds has the slides of tissues removed from Lynn Hawthorne at Ivory Hospital. He has to return them to Lowell to pass on to our expert witnesses, but before Reynolds does that, he wants me to examine them.

Within the hour I was back at my previous workplace, Pinnacle Hospital, looking at slides, just like the old days.

The slides I looked at were of specimens removed from Lynn Hawthorne at the time of her hysterectomy. I was hoping for a miracle—maybe the cancer is a metastatic cancer to the cervix from the lung, which would have nothing to do with missed Pap smears.

No such luck. It's a cancer of the cervix all right. I didn't have any significant disagreements with the interpretations and diagnoses of the Ivory Hospital pathologists.

Nevertheless, the findings were interesting. As I looked at the slides, two things amazed me:

1. How well-differentiated the cancer is. To look at it under the microscope, it looks very low grade, something not aggressive at

all, and that it would not recur or metastasize. If I didn't know what has happened to Ms. Hawthorne, I would have predicted such a low grade tumor would not cause any further problems for the patient whatsoever.

2. How small the original tumor in the cervix was. I measured it on the slide as invading into her tissues only 1.5 mm, or a little more than 1/20th of an inch! Indeed, Dr. Smith, the gynecologist/oncologist who performed the surgery was right: Ms. Hawthorne should have been cured by the hysterectomy.

Yet only five months later Lynn Hawthorne had metastases, a death sentence. Truly. Unfortunately. Amazing.

Thursday, December 4, Year 1

I talked to Lowell today. He wants copies of the Pap smear requisition forms, which came with Lynn Hawthorne's Pap smears. I called our cytoprep person at Pathology Services, who said she could find them for me. Lowell wants to meet with me on Monday, so I will bring them with me then.

Friday, December 5, Year 1

We heard from Dr. Gable of Arkansas, who thinks the Pap smears of Lynn Hawthorne are negative. He agrees with the interpretations of our lab, and that our lab did not make a mistake in the interpretations of Lynn Hawthorne's Pap smear. Since Arkansas is a state contiguous to ours, he is eligible as an expert witness for us.

Of course, this is great news. Dr. Gable is a world-class expert on Pap smears.

We also have the results of the South Carolina study, which also confirmed that we did not make a mistake.

More and more it looks like we can mount a credible defense.

Sunday, December 7, Year 1

Reynolds told me he ran into Dr. Mary Bishop, the plaintiff's gynecologist, at the hospital the other day while Mary was making rounds.

Mary was dressed in a camouflage suit and was obviously going hunting after she finished seeing her patients. "Boy, it sure is a bad deal," said Mary, speaking about the lawsuit, "a real shame it's come to this. I want it settled." Mary is quite the hunter and softball player. Remember, this is Texas.

Monday, December 8, Year 1

I met with Lowell for an hour today. We went over the record of my deposition and I made a few minor changes, just typos really.

Then he showed me the answers to some of Scott Francis's interrogatories. I made a few corrections.

Lowell asked me who was the technical supervisor of Bruce Palmore and Billy Swenson. I told Lowell that I was.

Lowell replied, "In the opinion of Dr. Gable, that you were only available by phone is a weakness."

"I'm afraid he has a very academic view of things, not necessarily related to the real world," I said.

I also returned to Lowell the slides and reports of Ms. Hawthorne's specimens from Ivory, so he could pass them on as indicated. Lowell was irritated that Reynolds had made some notes on the reports.

"Can I attend the depositions of Dr. Roundtree and Dr. Pelton?" I asked.

"Yes, you can keep them in line," he answered. "How do you think they will do?"

"Pelton needs to be told not to take the high road. He can't say things like 'the chickens have come home to roost,' or 'I knew that something like this would happen.' He needs to know that if he sells Billy, Bruce, and us down the river, he will go right along with us."

"He's mad," said Lowell. "He wants to be dropped from the suit."

"He should be. So should Larry. So should Reynolds. So should I."

"I told Dr. Pelton I don't make the rules or decisions."

"I understand. I hope Pelton does."

"How do you think Larry Roundtree will do?"

"Who knows? In Larry's mind he will do great. Once upon a time we had a Joint Commission Inspection at Suburban Hospital, and Larry, as director of the laboratory at that time, was interviewed by the inspector. When I asked him how it had gone, Larry said that it had gone great, that they had just sat around shooting the bull, passing time. Later, when I saw the written report by the inspector, it had actually been a disaster, with a long list of deficiencies, so bad that we did not get the usual two-year accreditation, but that there would be a reinspection in three months. The CEO of the hospital put me in charge and made me laboratory director. It took a lot of work to get the lab straightened out, ready for the next inspection, which we passed with flying colors. So I have no idea how he will do at this deposition. Larry is a master at getting out of tight spots, so I don't know how he will act when he is actually in one, and a deposition is definitely a tight spot."

Lowell and I then had some words about my deposition, specifically with what I said when Francis asked me about my interpretation of Lynn Hawthorne's Pap smears. Francis and I had jousted for some time about it, but my essential answer was that "I'm not in a position to say at this time." It had been months since I had seen the slides, and I did not write out a report. Since then they had been all over the place, with widely varying interpretations. In the deposition I did say that "I believe I saw some abnormal cells in one or more of the Pap smears." Not a great answer, I concede, but an honest one.

"I'm uncomfortable with those answers," said Lowell. "I don't think you are credible."

"I'm not believing this!" I said. "I'm uncomfortable too. I wish I had testified that the Pap smears were totally negative, but I couldn't, under oath, because I did see some abnormal cells retrospectively. The majority of experts who have looked at these slides have called them negative— look at the South Carolina study."

"What about Shelton over at Catholic, and Harris over at Christian… and who was it over at that other lab?"

"Rob Hall."

"Right. They clearly saw abnormal cells."

"And Gable called these Pap smears negative."

Lowell reluctantly nodded.

"I think you are finding that interpreting Pap smears is very subjective," I said.

Lowell reluctantly nodded again.

CHAPTER 14

Tuesday, December 9, Year 1

Reynolds phoned me this morning and wanted to know all about my meeting with Lowell. I filled him in. Reynolds thinks the case will be settled. "Francis strikes me as a basically lazy guy who will take the money if offered."

Today I received three letters from Lowell:

1. A draft of responses to the plaintiff's request for admissions. I saw a draft of it yesterday, and Lowell had made the changes I suggested.

2. A copy of some more documents we have turned over to Scott Francis so far, including my curriculum vitae. It sure seems like we have turned over a lot of documents to the other side, without getting anything in return. It has been months since this lawsuit was filed, and to this minute I do not know what proof they have that we messed up. Doesn't a plaintiff eventually have to prove the allegations, with expert witnesses and such?

3. The last letter was a copy of a letter to Dr. Gable accompanying the tissue slides for him to look at. Also, Lowell had included the requisition slips he had asked for.

I figured out the reason Dr. Gable wanted the slips. Dr. Gable thinks he sees some endometrial cells in one of the Pap smears, which can masquerade as abnormal cells. However, if the Pap smear was obtained during certain times in the menstrual cycle, e.g., during the bleeding phase, the presence of such cells would be normal. According to the requisition, Lynn Hawthorne had a recent menstrual period to explain the cells in question. Good catch by him. I guess that's why he is a world-class expert. I hope he stays on our side.

Wednesday, December 10, Year 1

I received two more letters from Lowell today. They do pile up.

The first was just another FYI about the correction sheet for the record of my deposition. No big deal.

However, the second letter is a big pain. We have to turn over to the plaintiff a copy of our most recent College of American Pathologists inspection, from over two years ago, the one that would be applicable to the time period of Ms. Hawthorne's Pap smears. I have already given all this information to Lowell, but he says "the dates are illegible" and he has only one page "page eight of thirteen." He wants to know where the other twelve pages are.

Well, yes, his copy is illegible, because my copy is illegible, the only copy I have. I don't have the originals. As far as there only being one page, that is because there was only one page pertaining to cytology, because we only had one deficiency; the remaining pages concern chemistry, hematology, urinalysis... the rest of the laboratory at Pinnacle Hospital lab, which was inspected at the same time as our Pathology Services lab, so those "missing" pages have nothing to do with cytology or Pap smears.

Notwithstanding my protests, Lowell wants it all, a legible copy of the page he has, and the whole report.

I looked in my files at home for an hour before I gave up; I don't have what he wants. It would have been nice if this had come up earlier, say March or April, when I still worked at Pathology Services and was on the medical staff at Pinnacle Hospital, and I had some clout.

Why am I doing all the work? Good question. Answer: Because otherwise it would not get done.

My next step was to call every applicable person at Pathology Services, to no avail. The College of American Pathologist (CAP) inspection records are not there.

So I phoned the director at Pinnacle Hospital laboratory to see if she could help. She was unavailable. I left a message to call me.

My next step was to call Reynolds, who was working at Pinnacle Hospital today, and I asked if he could help. He didn't have the records, or know where they were, but said he would try to find the Pinnacle lab director and have her give me a call.

Reynolds said, "Lowell and I really had words about our admissions. I do *not* want to take the hits for Billy and Bruce. Why should we take the hits? I really got into it with Lowell yesterday, and I don't care. Lowell is really pissed off at me, and I don't care. I mean, why should we accept the liability for these guys?"

Friday, December 12, Year 1

The Pinnacle laboratory director still hasn't phoned me. I phoned her yet again today, for at least the third time, and once again she was not available. I left another message to call me.

Then Reynolds phoned me. He was astonished that the Pinnacle lab director still had not called.

Next I called Lowell's office. He was unavailable, so I left a message.

Around noon Lowell returned my call. I filled him in on the difficulties I was having running down the CAP inspection report from two years ago. I said, "I don't know of any rule or law that says we have to keep this stuff, and Reynolds doesn't know of any rule or law that says we have to keep this stuff, and I really resent having to do Francis's work for him. *He* can call the CAP office and damn well run down the report himself if he wants it so bad."

In his sanctimonious voice Lowell answered, "Now, Jack, Scott Francis has every right to ask for any inspection data we have, and we have an obligation to produce it. Now I can't in good conscience tell him we haven't got this CAP data when I know we do. Now if he asks me for something out of line, I'll object. But I can't object to this."

"I haven't got it," I said.

"What do you mean you haven't got it? You had it last March or April."

"Right, and now it's December. I can't find it in my records, and even if I do, my copy isn't going to be any better than the one you already have. The originals are in the CAP offices in Chicago."

"Keep trying."

I so much resent Lowell's patronizing tone, like a parent talking to a young child, and I vented to Sarah, who explained it to me with one simple sentence: "Those lawyers stick together."

Of course. Lowell Pound has more loyalty to Scott Francis than he does to me. They both went to law school, probably the same one, both work for law firms, belong to the Bar, have the same background, probably have drinks together after work. Long after this case is over and Lowell is through with me, he will still have to deal with Scott Francis. Lowell can alienate me, but he can't alienate Francis.

Tuesday, December 16, Year 1

My last day of Film/Screenwriting classes today—semester break until next year. I write because I feel that writing is calling me, and medicine is rejecting me. I have been amazed at the aplomb with which my fellow physicians took the news over the last few months. Exactly one, my best friend, an internist, questioned my decision and tried to talk me out of leaving medicine. "Medicine needs your expertise," he said, "and you need medicine."

A more common response is to confide in me that they are contemplating leaving medicine as well. I was talking to a radiologist when he was performing a myelogram on me, and he told me that I was the topic of numerous lunchtime conversations in the doctors' lounge, always with envy.

It has been exciting to be with these film students about half my age. They call me Dr. Jack. In many ways they remind me of myself, thirty years ago. Most are gung ho and eager to learn.

There are differences, though. Few are as intense as I was. There is not the urgency to learn and succeed quickly that I felt at their age.

The difference in our ages showed up in our projects. My classmates' film and writing projects are about sex and/or violence. That's what they know, or at least are interested in. My projects tended to be about medicine or family, what I know.

Film school is similar to medical school. The format is similar: give the students the books and material they need, throw in a few lectures and directions, and let the students go to it. As in medical school, the pace is fast. Also, as in medical school and residency, much of the learning is from fellow students. I picked up things fast enough. I got either As or Bs in all my courses.

Most of my classes were at night. I tried to finish my assignments when I got home, when everything was fresh, and since I had classes for four separate subjects a week, I didn't want assignments to pile up. Often I worked into the early morning hours and then slept late the following day. That was not ideal. The way our family used to function was that our three boys went to school, I went to work, and Sarah took care of everything else. Now here I was, hanging around the house—sleeping, writing, and eating. I was in Sarah's house, her place of work, and I quickly got on her nerves. She is about as happy with me hanging around the house as I would be if she was hanging around the lab while I was working. "I married you for better or worse, but not for lunch" about summed it up.

It's hard knowing the effect of my career change on my three sons. They are high school and college students. None of them is going into medicine. They saw my lifestyle and didn't want any part of it.

Everyone in the family did pitch in to help me with my Film Production One project, either as actors or camera operators. My youngest son was the lead actor. The teacher was impressed by his acting.

Time has slowed down. At some holiday parties I saw some of my physician friends; I have been away from medicine for three months and it seems like three years.

Being a film student is not all good. The loss of employer-provided health insurance is a blow. I did COBRA to provide continuation of our family health insurance, but I have to pay the entire premium in after-tax dollars. Ouch. And when that coverage runs out after eighteen months, I will have to come up with something else.

And oh, do I miss that paycheck. I'm here to tell you that medicine, for all its drawbacks, pays well. It's a field where someone with some talent makes a reasonably good income. Writing is not like that. I know most of the writers in Dallas, and some are my friends. Even the best writers in Dallas, who are really good with a ton of talent and a good work ethic, don't make a living writing, but have to supplement their income with other jobs, like teaching.

Monday, December 22, Year 1

I have a lot of catching up to do in this diary. Last Wednesday I had an anterior cervical discectomy, a neck operation, and a right carpal tunnel release, a wrist operation. The anterior cervical discectomy is an operation to remove some bone and cartilage in the spine of my neck, which was pressing against a nerve. The right carpal tunnel release involved cutting and releasing a ligament in the wrist, which was compressing a nerve. Both conditions are probably related to my job—the neck degenerative disease secondary to years of looking through a microscope under conditions of high stress, and the wrist injury secondary to years of moving slides across a microscope stage, and dissecting.

The procedures were done at Pinnacle Hospital, and I was admitted overnight. Therefore, several of my former colleagues came to the room to visit, which was nice, but problematic. I tried to sit up and be sociable, but I think I did too much, and my wrist in particular is quite sore.

Today is the first day I have been able to write. I have a bandage on my right hand and a soft brace around my neck, making it difficult to do much of anything. I will not be able to write long. My hand is already a little sore and I don't want to push it.

I am trying to read my film history textbook to get a head start on the next semester of film school. I will take Film History I, Film Art, and Film Production Two.

Tuesday, December 23, Year 1

Back to the lawsuit. I received a letter from Lowell. In it was a copy of a letter he sent to Darlene Harvey, M.D., a cytopathologist in Oklahoma, another contiguous state, and a well-known expert regarding Pap smears. Lowell sent the Pap smears in question to her to interpret. Maybe she will be as helpful to us as Dr. Gable.

I do get tired of the hard time Lowell gives me, but I will say this: he is doing a lot of work for us, finding experts for us and defending us.

The depositions of John Pelton and Larry Roundtree were scheduled for today. Thinking I needed to attend those depositions, I did not schedule a follow-up appointment for today with the neurosurgeon who did my operations; today was the only day he had available before he heads to Europe, so it will be next year before he can see me.

Then, yesterday afternoon, around 4 p.m., I got a call from Lowell Pound's assistant telling me that, "The depositions set for tomorrow have been cancelled. Mr. Francis has the flu."

So I cancelled my appointment with my neurosurgeon for nothing. My first rule of lawsuits: nobody knows anything.

It bothers me to wonder what Lynn Hawthorne's thoughts are. I am sad to say this is probably her last Christmas and New Year's Eve, and I'm working against her. Why can't we just settle this case for a million dollars or so and provide this woman some peace. This lawsuit cannot be giving her any comfort, the direct opposite, I suspect. What a system, which makes me, a former healer, her adversary in her dying days.

Sick, really sick.

CHAPTER 15

Wednesday, December 24, Year 1

I'm still recovering, so I watched a movie, *The Apprenticeship of Duddy Kravitz,* a good movie, another one for you to check out. It's a coming-of-age film about an ambitious young man (played by a very young Richard Dreyfuss) set in Canada. In it a businessman old enough to be Duddy's father befriends him and becomes a mentor. There was some fascinating dialogue, applicable to my situation. The businessman, in the salvage business, tells of an accident in which one of his workers died on the job, a very serious matter, and there was talk of "negligence," and even going to jail. The businessman, Duddy's mentor, had to betray his business partner to escape punishment. His partner went to prison. "I was a little smarter than him," said Diddy's friend.

Totally applicable to my situation. My so-called colleagues, including two ob/gyn physicians, are obviously smarter than me, quickly betraying me to Ms. Hawthorne so that my company and I will pay, and they will survive. And someone has to pay. Our society demands it.

In our case, I contend that everyone is blameless—the gynecologist who discovered the cancer, the oncologist who treated the cancer, the cytotechnologists who looked at the Pap smears, our company, the patient herself, me, and my partners. No one messed up. But in our society, someone will have to pay for the fact that this single mom with a young daughter who has a good work ethic is going to die a painful death. That can't just happen. There has to be some balance. If she suffered, we have to suffer.

This sense of balance must be something intrinsic to the human spirit and is not new, present since the beginning of time. In Polynesian South Pacific the trope is that when a volcano erupted, someone had to be sacrificed, usually a young virgin, to restore balance and stop the volcano eruption so that the community could be saved. This may be a trope, but this legend probably has some basis in fact.

In the primitive societies living in the jungles of New Guinea, where I have been, sacrifices are needed to restore balance. Nelson Rockefeller's son, who disappeared there, was probably killed and eaten to restore balance with respect to the incursions and resultant killings as white civilization advanced on the native people.

If you want to get theological about it, this truth is in the Bible. Jesus was crucified and buried to atone for our sins and restore balance. He then rose from the dead so the community of believers could go on.

This theme is well described in Russell Banks's book *The Sweet Hereafter*, assigned reading in film school. The plot goes like this: On a snowy icy winter day in the north, a school bus skids from the highway and on to a lake, frozen at the surface. The ice breaks and the bus sinks into the water, and the schoolchildren are horribly injured or killed. The bus driver survives. It's an accident, but someone has to be blamed. It can't just happen. As the book asks "When the worst thing happens, whom do you blame?" The press searches for someone to blame. Tort lawyers from out of town show up, ready to file lawsuits against anyone with deep pockets—the state for the faulty highway or a faulty retaining fence, the bus manufacturer for making a substandard vehicle… someone, anyone, who can pay, who must pay, so that the victims, and their attorneys, can get justice. The book is a morality play, and one of the surviving students, crippled from the accident and in a wheelchair, lies under oath, pointing the finger at the bus driver, testifying falsely that the bus driver was speeding. The bus driver is a poor, relatively old working woman with limited resources and no future. She has nothing really. So forget about cashing in, forget about the lawsuits—even if she is found negligent, there is nothing to get, nothing to confiscate, no assets, no insurance, nothing. The press moves on. The lawyers leave. The community goes on. The bus driver is sacrificed to the volcano to restore balance.

I'm the bus driver.

Friday, December 26, Year 1

My neck and wrist are healing. It's great to be able to write again without pain.

Today I received a copy of a letter Lowell sent to Dr. Darlene Harvey in Oklahoma. Lowell evidently has sent her the slides of the specimens removed from Lynn Hawthorne by Dr. Smith at Ivory. Hopefully she can help with our defense. She is a woman and that is a plus. I really don't want the jury to see a group of men on our side against a lone woman on the other side.

I was finally able to lay my hands on the CAP inspection documents and I mailed them to Lowell.

Wednesday, December 31, Year 1

Reynolds called this morning, waking me up. He was very interested in my anecdotes about trying to run down the CAP inspection report, especially the part about how Lowell felt that Scott Francis "had every right to it."

Reynolds said, "If Scott Francis becomes a judge, Lowell doesn't want to get on his bad side."

In fact, for quite some time Reynolds has been fed up with Lowell, even though he was Reynolds's choice to defend us. Reynolds is angry that Lowell keeps taking the "high road" and refusing to try a defense that Bruce Palmore and Billy Swenson, our cytotechnologists, were independent contractors. Also it bothers Reynolds that Lowell has said to him that the "plaintiff deserves something."

I agree. Our attorney is supposed to be defending us, and I think he should be 100% behind us, not halfway. I am sure Scott Francis is not telling the plaintiff anything to the effect that "they have a good lab run by good well-trained doctors who have a clean record with no malpractice judgments or settlements—let's cut them some slack and make a reasonable settlement offer." Unlike Lowell, Scott Francis is 100% behind Lynn Hawthorne.

Reynolds is also worried about how John Pelton will do during his deposition. "He is so... arrogant," said Reynolds. "Instead of saying 'I don't know' or 'I can't remember,' I'm afraid he will give long convoluted answers that will bury us. I finally had to call Lowell to get him in line. Evidently he had some success, because after Lowell met with

Pelton, Pelton said, 'If Lowell's purpose was to tick me off, he succeeded,' so I think Pelton will be okay. I told him that ninety percent of his answers should be 'I don't know,' and the other ten percent should be 'I don't remember.'"

Reynolds sounded in good spirits. I kind of miss practicing with him. It was never dull.

Later in the day Reynolds called again to talk about the CAP inspection data, and to make sure that when the other side names their expert witnesses that we get their inspection data. When it comes to obeying rules and regulations, or anything else, I'll put our lab up against anybody.

Tuesday, January 6, Year 1

Today I received a letter from Lowell, which is a copy of the plaintiff's second request for admissions. I'm not an attorney, but my understanding is that these documents are literally admissions, that both sides, plaintiff and defendant, agree on. At any rate these admissions are as follows:

"If Billy Swenson's examination of Lynn Hawthorne's pap (sic) smear three years ago did not comply with the recognized standard of acceptable professional practice applicable to him, then that failure is imputed to Pathology Services, P.C., as a matter of law."

Exactly the same language is used for Bruce Palmore's Pap smear interpretation.

In Lowell's cover letter he says, "I believe we have to admit these… requests. Please let me know if you feel differently about this."

Well, I *do* feel differently about this. I am willing to take *some* of the responsibility for what our cytotechs did, but I am not willing to concede that I, or our company, should take all of that responsibility. Suppose, just for the sake of argument, that evidence emerges that these two gentlemen were drunk when they examined these Pap smears for us. In that case I think you could possibly make the case that some of the responsibility should belong to us at Pathology Services, P.C., and that we should have done a better job of supervising them, and been more discerning in hiring them… whatever. But if they were drunk and didn't do the job that we were paying them for, at least some of the responsibility should be borne by them.

I called Reynolds to express these thoughts to him. He agreed and said, "Lowell and I go round and round on this stuff, and I am just tired of it. Why don't you write a letter to Lowell and explain why you disagree with him."

So, I will. After all, I'm supposed to be a writer.

Wednesday, January 7, Year 1

I mailed the letter today. In it I asked, "Is this a Kafka novel?" Then I proceeded to tell him that I disagreed with his admissions, and why. I finished the letter with "But you're the lawyer."

Friday, January 9, Year 1

Today I received a response to my letter, so Lowell had obviously written a reply the day he received it. His angry letter is over three pages! Here are the highlights:

"Dear Jack:

I am writing to respond to your January 6 letter.

This is not a Kafka novel; it is a very serious medical malpractice lawsuit in which you, your former colleagues, and Pathology Services have been sued for $10 million.

Let me review some facts for you…

Do you really want to tell a jury in this case that Pathology Services should have no responsibility for the quality of the examination and interpretation of Lyn (sic) Hawthorne's pap (sic) smears? If you do, I think a jury will be outraged at you, your colleagues, and your laboratory… To suggest that you can provide pap (sic) smear screening services to the public and profit from them but not accept responsibility when those services are not performed in accordance with the standard of care is an absurd position.

Your laboratory "might" have been able to take this position if the relationship between Swenson/Palmore and the laboratory had been clear and unambiguous. Unfortunately, it is not!

… Under the facts we are dealing with in this case, I do not believe you can make a credible argument that the laboratory is not responsible for the examination and interpretation of Ms. Hawthorne's pap (sic) smears.

I would be happy to discuss this with you on the telephone or personally if you care to do so…"

These excerpts capture the tone of the letter. Copies were sent to Milton Jackson, Reynolds Price, Larry Roundtree, and John Pelton.

After reading the letter, I immediately phoned Lowell, but he was on another line.

I phoned Reynolds and asked him if he had seen Lowell's letter. "I thought it was bizarre," he said.

"Good word for it."

"But like you said, 'he's the lawyer.'"

By that time it was close to 2 p.m. and it was time for my weekly meeting for coffee with Tim Anderson—friend, mentor, and favorite poet. This is a meeting I never miss.

Later, at 4:40 p.m., I was finally able to talk to Lowell. "Remind me not to write you any more letters," I said.

He seemed genuinely surprised. "Why?"

"Because it generated a three-page reply, and not a very nice one. But as I said, you're the lawyer, and I accept your judgment."

"It's the weekend. Any good movies you would recommend?"

"*Boogie Nights.*"

"I hear it's good."

"It is."

"I have good news for you. Dr. Darlene Harvey in Oklahoma is going to help us. She did not see cancer in any of the Pap smears."

"Yes!"

"But the thing most helpful to us is the South Carolina study where practicing supervisory cytotechnologists signed out the Pap smears as negative."

"Thank you for all the help you are giving us."

"I'm not sure it will make much difference in the final outcome."

"I'm well aware that the plaintiff will have the sympathy of the jury."

Thursday, January 15, Year 1

I received copies of two letters today:

One is a letter from Scott Francis to Lowell, complaining that our answers to the plaintiff's fourth request for production didn't have all the requested info. The letter concludes "Please let me know whether or not you will agree to provide the information. Otherwise I will have to seek the court's intervention."

The second letter is from Lowell to Scott Francis, with a similar tone, quarrelling over the timetable to take the depositions of Larry Roundtree and John Pelton. Part of it says "I plan to have Dr. Roundtree and Dr. Pelton available in my office for their depositions on January 20 as we previously discussed. If you refuse to take their depositions at that time, then you can explain that to the judge. I previously made these doctors available to you on December 23 about three weeks ago, and you cancelled the depositions because you said you were sick."

It's like two schoolchildren quarrelling, and each threatens to go to the teacher and tattle. What a way to make a living.

I got home from film classes tonight at 9:30 p.m., and Sarah gave me a message to call Lowell Pound tomorrow. Probably bad news.

Friday, January 16, Year 1

Bad news all right. Lowell doesn't like the CAP inspection data that I went to such great pains to find. We had *one* deficiency, and the checklist has several hundred questions regarding Pap smears. The one deficiency was that we needed to "*document* attempts to obtain follow-up." This pertains to the need to make sure that the gynecologist does proper follow-up on any abnormal Pap smear report that comes from our lab—the gynecologist does a biopsy, repeat Pap smear, resection, something.

That's it, out of the whole daylong inspection. The inspector actually verbally conceded that we were doing appropriate follow-up, but that we needed to document what we were doing in a better fashion.

Fair enough.

But then what happened is that this one deficiency generated CAP computer verbiage, which had nothing to do with our lab or our inspection, but reaffirming the need for quality assurance, quality control, and so on—for education purposes only, not applying to our lab. Getting a jury to understand this, when Scott Francis is doing his best to get the jury not to understand this, will be tough.

"When the plaintiff's attorneys finally tell us who their expert witnesses are, do we get to see the CAP inspection results of *their* labs?" I asked.

"Probably not."

"And you wonder why I call this a Kafka novel."

Lowell had some technical questions, and he wants me to run down some more editions of the CAP checklist.

"I still don't understand why we have to do Scott Francis's work for him," I said.

"I'm sorry. Dr. Pelton and Dr. Roundtree are giving their depositions January 20."

"I'll be there."

Also today there was a letter from Lowell in the mail, containing copies of medical records from the University of Iowa Medical Center where Lynn Hawthorne is being treated. Her medical condition continues to worsen from really bad to horrible. The most significant finding was a CT scan demonstrating "destruction of the right hemi sacrum [tailbone] most likely from residual or recurrent tumor."

There are a lot of nerves in this area, so no doubt she is in great pain. My eyes are tearing up and that's all the writing I can do today.

CHAPTER 16

Tuesday, January 20, Year 1

Today I attended the depositions of John Pelton and Larry Round-tree. As usual, getting there was an adventure, with logistical and scheduling snafus. The depositions were scheduled for 9 a.m., and I arrived about 8:25 a.m. After fighting morning traffic to go downtown, I had to park in the underground garage of Lowell's skyscraper office building, where the signs read "Tenant Parking Only." I needed to have my parking ticket stamped and validated so I could park there, hopefully for free.

Well, getting my ticket stamped was just about more than Lowell's law firm could do. The receptionist couldn't do it. She had to call in someone more qualified, announcing on the phone that "Jack Spence" was here. I took a seat in the reception area.

While I waited, the receptionist answered the phone, which was ringing as fast as she could answer it. The answers to each phone call were exactly the same and went like this: "… Law Firm… He's not in… Can I have him call you?" Then she would write down a phone number on her memo pad.

After a wait of about ten minutes, a woman wearing a black dress, in her mid-fifties, came and stamped my parking ticket. It was still not ready to present to the parking attendant. She said, "Lowell's secretary needs to put a number on it, and she's on the telephone." Then she left.

About another ten minutes passed, and Lowell's secretary, a tall blonde woman, walked up to me and said, "I'm Janie, Lowell's assistant. When I came in this morning, there was a note to call you and tell you that you didn't need to be here till 9:45."

"The depositions are at 10?"

"Yes."

Janie wrote a number on the back of my parking ticket, so at least I accomplished that. I had about an hour to kill.

"Have you had breakfast?" asked Janie.

I had, so she escorted me to the large conference room I had been in before when I had given my deposition. Janie walked to a coffee machine in the far left corner and poured me a cup. Then she left.

Having nothing better to do, I took a closer look at the room. There was a sink next to the coffee machine, so I washed my hands. There were a couple of chandeliers over the large wood table. However, most of the light came from twenty recessed lights shining from the white tile ceiling. Drawn light white curtains covered the floor-to-ceiling windows separating the conference room from the corridor. I walked across the room to part the curtains and look across the corridor through more floor-to-ceiling windows, and I saw the beautiful plains of North Texas, from twenty-seven floors up.

A little before 10 a.m., John Pelton, my former employee pathologist, arrived, as did my former partner, Larry Roundtree. I sat between Larry and John.

Lowell Pound entered the room and sat across from us. He looked directly at John. John is a mildly pudgy man of average height, light brown hair combed straight back, glasses with light frames, and has the look of a high school science teacher. "Dr. Pelton," said Lowell, "for the next few hours your fate is in your hands. There is nothing I can say or do from this point on. It's up to you."

"Keep my coffee cup full and I'll be fine," said John.

John's coffee cup was kept full, and he did fine. It got off to a rough start, though. One of the first questions from Scott Francis was about whether John has a curriculum vitae; John pulled one out of his sport coat pocket and gave it to him! Lowell about had a heart attack. He had not seen John's CV, and rule number one of a deposition is not to bring documents that the other side can examine. Leave that to your attorney, for many reasons, not the least of which is so that your attorney can vet it. Lowell snatched the CV from John's hands and looked it over. Only then did he pass it on to Scott Francis.

From then on I thought John did great. However, it was frustrating for me to listen to Scott Francis's questions and not be able to say anything, to say "that's a trap." Sometimes Francis would let a question linger after it had been answered, tempting John to expand his answer and make a mistake. Also, Francis would rephrase the same question over and over again, to try to beat John into changing his answer, and I wanted to shout, "Don't weaken. Stand your ground." It was like sitting next to an alcoholic who had a glass of whisky in front of him and I am silently imploring him not to take that drink.

After an hour and twenty minutes of questions, we took a break. Lowell told Larry and me not to talk to John during the break. Wouldn't you know it that in the reception area Larry and I ran into John, and we were the only people around. "How am I doing?" John asked. We both gave him a thumbs-up, but we didn't say anything.

The deposition then resumed. Lowell sat next to John, taking notes on a legal pad with white paper. When he was not writing, he sat with his right elbow on the table and his chin in his right hand. Lowell had an interesting tactic: when the questioning was not to Lowell's liking, he would "object to form" and then explain the objection in such a way that it was obvious how John was supposed to answer. Francis got more and more irritated about this and finally exclaimed, "I wish, Lowell, that you would just say 'object to the form,' and if I want you to explain it, I'll ask you to explain it, okay?"

It got more heated. Here is from the transcript:

MR. FRANCIS: Lowell, again I'm going to ask you just to object to the form of the question.

MR. POUND: You just go right ahead. Because you keep mixing everything up, and every one of those questions is faulty because nobody knows what you mean. So I'm just going to let you tread along here down a path where your questions and the responses are meaningless.

The dispute reached a climax with some logbooks from our laboratory that had just been put into evidence, and whether John could answer questions about them, and whether there should be a postponement of the rest of the deposition. A postponement was the last thing any of us defendants wanted. We wanted to file a motion dismissing the individual pathologists from the case as soon as possible. This could only happen after our depositions, so all of us, including Lowell, wanted the depositions to end today. Lowell slammed the logbooks in front of Francis and here is the transcript:

MR. POUND: You go ahead and ask the questions you want. I'm not putting it off. Go ahead and ask them.

MR FRANCIS: With the logbooks.

Mr. Pound: You go ahead and ask all the questions you want to ask. We are going to get over this today. And if necessary, we'll just take a recess so that the witness can acquaint himself with the documents.

So another recess. During the break, Lowell served Francis with some papers on the case, a motion to schedule a hearing on our motion for summary judgment, and to get the names of the individual pathologists removed from the lawsuit. He slammed these papers in front of Francis as well, although not quite as hard as the logbooks.

The deposition resumed, and then it was over. It was time for a lunch break. John, Larry, Lowell, and I met in Lowell's office and ate sandwiches. Lowell said, "I hope that you don't mind that Francis really ticked me off."

"That was my favorite part," I said.

Everyone laughed.

"I'm just glad my part is over," said John. As he left, we all told John the truth: he did a good job. He was a rock defending our lab.

Larry's deposition began at 1 p.m., when he took John's place sitting across from Scott Francis. Lowell sat to Larry's left, and I sat across from Lowell, down the table a ways from Francis. The court stenographer sat at the head of the table between Francis and Larry.

Larry was wearing a white shirt with a subdued black and gold sport coat, with an emphasis on the black. The deposition did not go well. Larry is a tall handsome guy, in his mid-fifties, with dark brown hair combed straight back. He looks like a matinee movie idol, straight out of central casting to play the role of tall handsome doctor. At the beginning of the deposition, Larry played that role, leaning forward in an intimidating way, which has worked for him to get positions of authority and responsibility, and which has worked through the years when he has been working with people not as smart or good looking as he is.

Well, I don't know if Francis is smarter or better looking than Larry, but he certainly had the advantage in that he was asking the questions. After forty-five minutes Larry was not leaning forward, but backward, cowering. His voice, so confident at the beginning, was quavering.

It was bad, bad enough that every once in a while Lowell would look across the table at me, smile grimly, and look at the ceiling—usually when Larry would admit to something he shouldn't, like this exchange:

SCOTT FRANCIS: Have you been informed of how much income Pathology Services had three years ago, and four years ago, related to Pap screens or Pap smears?

LARRY: I'm sure I have been given that information.

Well, maybe Larry has been given that information, but I'm an owner too, and I sure don't know the answer to that question. Our income came from a potpourri of insurance companies, physicians, patients, and others, and they paid varying amounts—for example, we had discounts for prompt payment. On top of that, "income" would be revenue minus expenses, and I have no idea how we allocated rent, reagent cost, courier cost... to histology, surgical pathology, non-Pap smear cytology, Pap smear cytology, etc. We never ever came up with a good way to do that. We simply collected the money, paid our expenses, tried to save some money for capital expenditures, and tried to have some left over to pay ourselves some income. How much of the income was Pap smears is unknown as far as I know, so the correct answer would be "I don't know." If I had to guess, we probably lost money on Pap smears. We did them as a loss leader so we could get tissue biopsies from the clinicians who sent us Pap smears, and those biopsies were lucrative. Had there been a follow-up question like "How much revenue did you collect from Pap smears?" my answer would still be "I don't know," because I don't, although that information probably is available.

But his incorrect answer led to a bunch of other questions, which put Larry in even more of a defensive posture.

SCOTT FRANCIS: Where would this information be located?

LARRY: I would assume it would be—let's see. Where *would* that information be located? At this point in time, it's probably located on a computer disc in a warehouse.

There was question after question like this about this topic, and others, with similar answers. It got so bad that Lowell had to stop the proceedings, turn to Larry and say, "Dr. Roundtree, it does the court no good, nor your defense, nor even Mr. Francis, to answer questions with answers you 'assume' to be true, or 'think' might be true, or to answer what 'probably' might be the case... Those answers help no one, the plaintiff, the defense, or the court. If you know the answer, answer it. If you don't, say you don't know.

Good advice. For example, I don't have a clue what "computer disc" Larry was talking about, nor what "warehouse" he was talking about. Scott Francis made quite clear he wants this info and the disc, and made Larry promise he would find it and safeguard it. Good luck with that, Larry.

Lowell would also look at me, smile grimly, and look at the ceiling when Scott Francis would ask the same question over and over. Example:

> Q. Do you have any criticism of the—the way in which the slides were interpreted by either Mr. Swenson or Mr. Palmore?
>
> A. No.
>
> Q. Do you have any criticisms of the interpretations by either Mr. Palmore or Mr. Swenson?
>
> A. No.

Over and over the same group of questions would be asked and answered.

The best part of the day was that we are going to file a motion to get individual pathologists, including me, removed from the lawsuit, which will continue against Pathology Services. At least my name will be cleared.

CHAPTER 17

Thursday, January 22, Year 1

Today I received a letter from Lowell with copies of our responses to the plaintiff's second request for admissions. It goes like this:

"1. If Billy Swenson's examination of Lynn Hawthorne's pap [sic] smear in August four years ago did not comply with the recognized standard of acceptable practice applicable to him, then that failure is imputed to Pathology Services, P.C., as a matter of law."

The remainder of the document describes similar admissions.

Friday, January 30, Year 1

Reynolds Price called this morning. "How did John and Larry do at their depositions?" he asked.

"What did Larry say?"

"He said they went well."

"Have you asked Lowell how they went?"

"Yes."

"What did he say?"

"Pretty much the same thing he said about yours and mine, that there were some things that Lowell would have answered differently, but overall they went fine."

"I thought John did great. About Larry's, I will defer to Lowell, but read the depositions and see what you think."

I think the case will be quiet for a while. Lowell says he wants to settle the case, but says Lynn Hawthorne's attorneys aren't interested at all, that he can't get Francis to even talk about settling the case.

Tim Anderson wrote a poem for me:

"Exercise The Prudence

> In Jurisprudence
> For Jack Spenser, M.D.
> Don't even go see your own lawyer without an attorney."

> It will be in his next book. The autographed page says this:
> "To
> my friend and fellow writer
> Jack Spenser,
> Love
> Your humble poet
> Tim C. Anderson"

It's now framed and on a wall in my study.

Thursday, February 18, Year 2

I was right about the break in the action. Nothing has happened for weeks.

Today I received a study from the chairman of the Department of Economics and Business Administration at Ivory University, which calculates the pecuniary loss for Lynn Hawthorne to be $471,990.

We have a settlement offer on the table for more than that.

Tuesday, February 24, Year 2

I received a letter from Lowell saying that Ms. Hawthorne and her attorneys, Dale Lichty and Scott Francis, have decided to "voluntarily dismiss" Larry, Reynolds, John, and me from the lawsuit. The case against Pathology Services will proceed.

For us to be dropped, we have to withdraw our motion of summary judgment. A no-brainer to drop the motion—there is no way it would be granted.

In the letter Lowell says he has to hear from each one of us that we agree with this course of action. Another no-brainer. I phoned him åimmediately.

I am so relieved. Since I will be dropped as an individual, once more I will have a totally clean record, which means a lot.

Friday, March 13, Year 2

It's official. I am dropped personally from the lawsuit. Yippee! Today I received a copy of an "Order of Voluntary Non-Suit and Dismissal as to Certain Named Defendants," including Larry, Reynolds, John, and me.

The lawsuit against Pathology Services will continue, so this story is not over, and it will not be over until it is settled or goes to trial. I think it will be settled. In fact, I'm surprised it's not already settled.

The writing is going well. Charles Wilson, my TV writing teacher from last fall, has offered me a chance at a job. The Gravy Restaurant Chain based in Austin, Texas, is interested in producing a TV series called *Gravy*. The premise is that there is a male country music star who is on the road a lot, touring. He has a wife who, in episode one, dies of breast cancer, leaving behind three kids the country music star will have to raise as a single dad. The country music star decides to leave the road and stay home to raise the kids. To support the family, he decides to open a restaurant, which fortuitously looks like a Gravy Restaurant. The country music star will open and close each hour-long episode with a song sung on a porch that looks exactly like a Gravy Restaurant porch. A famous country music star has agreed to play the lead. The episodes will be filmed in a small town about an hour from here, which has already agreed to cooperate. They could use the industry. The vice president in charge of this project is Darlene Cox, and the head writer will be Charles Wilson. He is asking me and one other student from his class to be writers.

It sounds like old-fashioned entertainment. Growing up in a small Midwestern town in the fifties, I should be able to do this kind of writing, and contribute.

So, to prove to Darlene Cox that I can write comedy, I wrote a *Seinfeld* script and turned it in to Charles Wilson.

Friday, March 20, Year 2

One of the common themes in screenplays and movies is that one cannot escape the past. There are movies about con men who want to go straight, but get pulled into one last caper, and hit men who want to become store owners, actors, artists, or whatever, but can't leave the business until one last job. One of the best is the appropriately named *Out of the Past*, one of the best film noir movies. The protagonist, played by Robert Mitchum, in probably his best role, wants just to be a humble gas station attendant in a small town. Some of his previous associates find him, and he gets sucked in to dangerous intrigue.

In a gentler way, that is happening to me. I ran into a general surgeon at the gas station. "I wish you would come back," he said.

A few days ago I ran into Mary Bishop, Lynn Hawthorne's gynecologist, at the same gas station. Mary asked me how my writing was going, and did I miss pathology. I told her I missed the good parts of pathology, not the bad parts.

"Well, you can always come back to it," she said.

Charles Wilson and Darlene Cox liked my *Seinfeld* script. Then they wanted me to prove I can write drama, so I wrote a *Chicago Hope* screenplay. They liked that one too. It looks like I have a real job, a real writing job.

Wednesday, April 15, Year 2

I don't have a writing job. The Gravy Restaurant Company figured out that it's a heck of a lot easier to earn money making French toast for fifty cents and selling it for eight dollars, than losing millions of dollars on each episode of *Gravy* and trying to make it up in syndication fifteen to twenty years down the road. Darlene Cox was fired. Charles Wilson does not have the head writing job, and I do not have a writing job.

Thursday, April 16, Year 2

Out of the past, I got a phone call from Priscilla Catlin, Chief Operating Officer of our local American Red Cross Blood Services. When I was in private practice of pathology, I got to know her when I served as a volunteer for the American Red Cross—on the board, and on the Medical Advisory Committee. I have high regard for Priscilla Catlin.

"Our medical director is leaving, moving to North Carolina," she said. "Do you want to take her place?"

"I don't have my Boards in transfusion medicine," I said. "I'm just a general pathologist. I am not sure I can do the job. I haven't had much experience in blood banking."

"But you're smart. You can learn."

I believe in synchronicity in life, that forces come together to tell you what to do. Medicine and pathology burnt me up. Then the lawsuit came, and it was a bad climax of that episode of my life. It was obvious it was time to leave medicine and pathology—synchronicity.

So I left medicine to be a writer and a film student. I did that for eight months. I'm still doing that. Now, classes are ending for the semester, and I have taken all the writing classes at the school. I'm done there. My writing job with *Gravy* fell through and that's done too. That the writing project fell through is not that much of a surprise. It's show business and it happens all the time that projects get killed early or late in the process. It is rare to green-light a project when millions of dollars and many careers are at stake.

To make it in this line of work, writing for TV and film, I need to be in a place where there is a lot of this, where stuff is being produced all the time, so if one project falls through, there is always another one, and that place is not here. That place is Los Angeles, California.

I'm not moving there. Dallas is my home. I will stay here and be buried here.

Here and now, though, I am at a real crossroads. It's obvious which road to take.

Friday, May 1, Year 2

My first day on the job. I am the medical director for the American Red Cross Blood Services (ARC) in Dallas. The setting where I will be talking on the phone has changed dramatically. I have a fantastic corner office on the top floor of our Midtown building, with wraparound windows. On one side I see the tall downtown city hospitals, Christian Hospital and HCA Century Hospital, with thousands of patient rooms and tower parking. But the real treat is in the other direction, where I see downtown Dallas with its skyscrapers; it looks like the visual prologue to the TV show *Dallas*. The sun shines on the skyline, changing the lighting throughout the day. My favorite time is "Magic Hour" just before dusk, that favorite time for cinematographers to film a scene, because the colors are so vivid. The sunlight shines at a flat angle and bounces off the city with a golden hue that makes the city seem to float in the distance, like the magical city it is. I feel like J. R. Ewing.

Monday, June 8, Year 2

I haven't heard about the lawsuit for weeks, so today I phoned Lowell to find out what is going on. Scott Francis is trying to schedule the trial for June of next year. Lowell thinks that it is best to put off this case as long as possible.

"I went back into medicine," I said. "I'm the medical director for the American Red Cross Blood Services."

"I'm not surprised. You're a good doctor. Do your partners know?"

"I wouldn't be surprised if they did. The medical world is a small one, but I haven't told them."

Friday, July 17, Year 2

The case has been scheduled for trial beginning June 14 of next year, in front of Judge Hand. I have no idea what he is like, good or bad for us, but I think we can put up a credible defense.

Sarah brings me back to reality. "What's the plaintiff's health like these days?"

Good question and an important one. Lynn Hawthorne has metastases to her pelvic bones and will die a horrible death. She will lose her life and win her case.

I see no way this trial will happen in June of next year. None of our expert witnesses have been deposed. Nor have any of the plaintiff's expert witnesses been deposed. We don't even know who they are. Incredible. At this late date, year two of the lawsuit, the only work the plaintiffs have done to present their case is simply to assert that we messed up, by the testimony of the plaintiff, who is not an expert in the field—not a physician, pathologist, or cytotechnologists—and who, while sympathetic, is hardly unbiased. There has been no testimony from a single expert witness, from our side or the other side.

For this to go to trial, the plaintiff will eventually have to present evidence by expert witnesses, as will we. These witnesses, most of whom are physicians, are very busy, and so are the attorneys—so the depositions will be difficult to schedule. I think it will take months, probably years to get this done.

Saturday, August 1, Year 2

It has been a year since I attended Lynn Hawthorne's deposition. In it she mentioned that her current boyfriend was a fellow named Dan Jennings, whose family owns Jennings Signs. On my commute downtown I pass their establishment going to and from work. It's easy to notice. There is an impressive sign out front, which one should expect from a sign company. I have to look up, way up, to see it. It has neon blue letters against a black background. Of course, every time I see it, I think of Lynn Hawthorne.

Saturday, August 15, Year 2

Lowell is back to thinking settlement.

He forwarded to me the latest medical information about Lynn Hawthorne from her current doctor, an associate professor of gynecologic oncology at the University of Iowa Medical Center.

The medical news is horrible. Lynn Hawthorne has recurrent cancer, which is destroying her sacrum (tailbone). She also has a vesicovaginal fistula (a tract or tunnel running from her bladder to her vagina). Thus she is leaking urine from her bladder to her vagina. According to her oncologist, "She is beyond definitive therapy with either surgery or radiation therapy."

What a terrible way to live. What a terrible way to die.

Lowell also sent me a copy of a letter he sent to Milton Jackson, the Mutual Malpractice attorney. In it Lowell says, "… I feel that if we are going to attempt to settle this case, now is the best time to do it. The plaintiff's situation is hopeless. In my opinion a structured settlement for this lady that gave her up-front cash and secured her child's future would be an enticing offer that she might not want to pass up. I recommend that we begin to negotiate such a settlement now."

My thoughts: Give this unfortunate woman some money and some peace—now, before it is too late. This should have happened already. She is the only one in this whole matter who is acting with nobility and dignity.

Monday, August 24, Year 2

I continue to be amazed at the incompetence of Lowell's office. Today I received an envelope from Lowell with a copy of a letter sent to Dale Lichty, the plaintiff's attorney. It has three sentences: "This will acknowledge your letter of August 19. I have sent your letter to my client and to their insurance carrier. I will let you know their response as soon as possible."

That's it. No copy of a letter dated August 19 from Lichty. No thoughts from Lowell. Nothing.

This incident adds to the long list of snafus by Lowell's law office, which I have detailed in this diary. What makes me so judgmental about him is that Lowell is so judgmental about us. He never loses a chance to shake his head in scorn any time our documentation is not pristine, or our inspection results are not 100 percent perfect, or when not every reviewer agrees with our Pap smear interpretations… Look, I get that Lowell is just taking the position that it is better for him, an attorney on our side, to point out the weaknesses of our defense, rather than the other side. But the double standard really gets old.

So I phoned Lowell's office, and, as usual, he wasn't available. I was able to talk to his assistant, and in a very nice way, I informed her of the documents I was missing in Lowell's latest communication. She replied that she had mailed the packet to me, including Dale Lichty's letter and a copy of Lowell's four-page letter from Lowell to Milton Jackson at Mutual Malpractice detailing Lowell's thoughts on the proposal. I made clear, again in a very nice way, that somehow I didn't receive those two documents. She swears she put them in the mail, but will send me another copy.

Lowell's assistant was kind enough to tell me what is going on. Mr. Lichty has offered to settle the case for $1.2 million. Our counteroffer will be something like this: $500,000 up front. Then a structured settlement so that more money will come to Lynn Hawthorne's daughter as she gets older, such that the total settlement will approach a face value of $1 million, but the total up-front cost would be $750,000.

What sounds good to me about this is that the two sides do not seem that far apart. Hopefully this lawsuit will be settled soon.

CHAPTER 18

Wednesday, August 26, Year 2

It didn't take long to receive the detailed settlement paper; a packet arrived the next day. As I understand it, Lowell is recommending to Milton Jackson at Mutual Malpractice that we offer Lynn Hawthorne's nine-year-old daughter, Tara, $500,000 up front, as well as an additional structured settlement (as I understand it, an annuity) worth $250,000, $300,000 or $400,000, which would give her income for the rest of her life.

Although I'm sure no one cares, I am okay with that.

I'm sure no one cares about my feelings about the remainder of the packet either, but it really ticks me off—a copy of a long letter from Lowell to Milton Jackson detailing the present status of the case. In it Lowell says that Pathology Services, P.C., is a malpractice attorney's worst nightmare, a threat to any patient who comes near it, and never in his long history of defending doctors has he encountered such a collection of inept, incompetent, and negligent losers.

I am not quoting verbatim.

Still, I think some of what Lowell has written is unfair. He says, "The fact that two pap (sic) smears were misread by two part-time workers… will weigh heavily against us."

I contend that the slides were not misread, that we have Dr. Gable and Dr. Harvey, national experts, who say the slides were not misread—not to mention the South Carolina study in which cytotechnologist supervisors agreed with our interpretation.

On the other hand, maybe I am too sensitive about this, because there are other parts of the letter where I think he gives us too much credit. For example Lowell says, "I feel the likelihood of a defense verdict is no better than 30 to 40%." Well, I agree it is no better than 30–40%

if by that you mean that zero percent is no better than 30–40%, because zero percent is about what our chances of winning are, in my opinion. Lowell states in the letter: "With the jury, we will be faced with overwhelming sympathy for Ms. Hawthorne and her nine-year-old daughter, who are without fault." I totally agree. We will lose.

About settling the lawsuit, Lowell concludes, "I look forward to hearing from you soon since I believe time to be of the essence given Ms. Hawthorne's failing health."

Friday, August 28, Year 2

Yesterday I phoned Lowell's office, and as usual he wasn't available. I left word to call me back, and as usual, he didn't. In the chess game of this lawsuit, I haven't the status of a pawn.

I called Reynolds to vent. He agreed with my analysis that Lowell is determined to see us as a bad lab in spite of our abundant documentation and evidence to the contrary. Reynolds hasn't even bothered to call Lowell with his feelings about settling the case. "I've gotten tired of buggin' Lowell, and I'm sure Lowell is tired of being bugged."

The rest of my professional life is going well. The regional commissioner of the College of American Pathologists has asked me to be the deputy state commissioner for the state of Texas. I will help make assignments for CAP inspections and go to a yearly meeting of muckety-mucks in Chicago. The regional commissioner asked me to do it, saying, "Heck, you went to medical school here and trained here, and you've been around forever and know every pathologist in Texas; I think you'd be great." I have to go to Austin for a day of training.

Thursday, September 3, Year 2

I received copies of three letters today.

The first was a letter addressed to Reynolds from Lowell. The two of them must have had a discussion about how closely we supervised our cytotechnologists.

"Dear Reynolds:

Following our telephone conversation of September 1, I checked the dates that Swenson and Palmore [our cytotechnologists] screened pap [sic] smears. Two dates were Sundays. What does this mean insofar as the availability of a pathologist 'next door' at Suburban Hospital to confer with them if they wanted to do so?"

The second is a letter to Milton Jackson at Malpractice Mutual, updating him on Ms. Hawthorne's health. She has inoperable cervical cancer involving the sacrum, measuring "15 cm x 20 cm," which, converted to inches, is about six inches by eight inches. That is a big bad cancer.

The third is a copy of the letter to the director of South Carolina School of Medicine Cytotechnology group, which did the blind review of Ms. Hawthorne's Pap smear, the review in which the vast majority of supervisory cytotechnologists agreed with the interpretations of our laboratory. The gist of the letter is that Texas state law prohibits the use of medical expert witnesses who are not licensed to practice in our state or in states contiguous to our state—unless a similar witness is not available in our state or a contiguous state. South Carolina is not contiguous to our state, so we have to prove the expertise of the South Carolina Cytotechnology program is not available in Texas or a contiguous state. That should be easy to prove. I know of no other service in the world that does what they do, a blind review of Pap smears.

Interestingly, the other side has to present their expert witnesses by September 30. Finally we will know who is going to testify against us. It amazes me that one and a half years after filing the lawsuit and making allegations against us, the other side has not provided one shred of evidence that our laboratory was guilty of malpractice. Granted, they have proved that Ms. Hawthorne had a bad result, but a bad result is not necessarily malpractice. Good heavens, every patient eventually has at least one bad result: every patient dies. To prove malpractice, the other side will have to prove we were negligent, with some medical experts to back them up.

Look, I am sure the plaintiff's attorneys can do that, and find expert witnesses, who are physicians, who will say we messed up. I'm just surprised they haven't had to name them yet.

Wednesday, September 16, Year 2

The case fades from my mind for long periods of time, only to show up again. This is progress. When the lawsuit was first filed, it was on my mind all the time. I don't know why that is. My friends and others tell me it is just about money, not about me, and I think they are right. But it hurts. Maybe because I've always regarded myself as a hero. I was certainly brought up that way in my loving, but dysfunctional family. I was the oldest of four children, the one who always tried to keep the family strong; if only I was good enough, smart enough, athletic enough, things would be okay and not out of control. I had to always play to win, not to lose.

That upbringing has had its upsides. It has made me productive and a winner, getting the coveted spots in medical school, residency, and private practice. But being a hero has its downsides. It really hurts to be sued.

I think this attitude and this history are common among doctors. In medical school and private practice, I was surrounded by people just like me.

Anyway, it's been two weeks since my last diary entry, because there's been nothing to write. No one has contacted me nor asked for advice.

Until today. From Lowell I received a copy of a letter he sent to Dale Lichty, an offer to settle the case. In it, the claimant, Tara Hawthorne, nine years old, would get the following:

"**Cash at Settlement**
$500,000.00 cash settlement…
Educational Benefits:
Annual Certain Income
$25,000.00 per year, guaranteed 5 years, beginning nine years from now, increasing at 4% compounding annually.
Monthly Certain Income
$1,250.00 per month, guaranteed 5 years, beginning 8 years from now, increasing at 4% compounding annually.
Guaranteed Lump Sum Payment
$20,000.00 payable at age 21.
$25,000.00 payable at age 25.
$32,325.00 payable at age 30.

In summary the plaintiff and her daughter would receive guaranteed benefits in the amount of $793,977.00."

I'm not sure I have all the details, because I would think the terms "educational" and "guaranteed" need to be defined, but it looks to me that financially Lynn Hawthorne's daughter would be set for life. I'm sure that's what she wants, and I hope she has the strength and judgment in her very frail state to take this offer, or something like it, so she can die in peace.

Saturday, September 19, Year 2

Dale Lichty has rejected our settlement offer. That didn't take long. His letter to Lowell is short:

"Dear Lowell:

Thank you for your September 15 letter. When you broached the subject of settlement in August, I appreciated it, and it was my sincere hope, the hope of this entire office, and of Lynn Hawthorne, that the case could be settled promptly. That is why we made such a reduced offer ($900,000 lower than the original demand), without any intention of further negotiation. Naturally our office was extremely disappointed in the response.

If and when Lynn is able to consider your offer, I will be back in touch with you."

Very sincerely yours,
Dale L. Lichty

I hope Lynn Hawthorne is involved in the negotiations. My attitude toward attorneys is that they fill out the forms about decisions the client makes. That is an important job, for indeed the forms had better be right, but the main decisions have to be made by the client, and the client has to do the work. For better or worse, I have had a lot of attorneys in my life, good ones for the most part, but I have never run into the Perry Mason type of attorney, who not only proves I am innocent, but finds the guilty party.

The good attorneys I know make recommendations with reasons, and some advice about what may or may not happen with a certain course of action, with some degree of conviction. But the client has the last word. We all have to kill our own snakes. The attorneys file the motions, communicate with the court, make sure the filings are done, and the paperwork is in order, which is challenging, difficult work that has to be done right. But these actions are to confirm decisions clients make.

I think it has to be that way. A good attorney can defend you to death, but it is the client's death.

The stakes in this lawsuit are not quite so high, but they're high enough. So, I hope the conversation the plaintiff's attorneys is having with Ms. Hawthorne is that this is Mutual Malpractice's offer, and we may get a better one in the future or at a trial, but that will take time, and you may be dead by then.

Tuesday, October 6, Year 2

Weeks go by and no news about the case. I am six months into my new job at the American Red Cross. I think I am going to make it, although for a while I wasn't sure. The hardest part was not what I expected, but something else. To repeat: "It's not what you worry about that gets you, it's what you don't worry about that gets you." When I took the job, my biggest worry was that I did not have much experience in transfusion medicine, and I was afraid medical issues would come up that I could not handle. That has not been a problem. What has been the hardest part is learning the processes and procedures of the American Red Cross, with associated acronyms. There are countless blood services directives (BSDs) and blood services letters (BSLs) that fill up several shelves in my office, and I had to get training and pass tests regarding every one. There are procedures for material review boards (MRBs), suspected post transfusion infection investigations (SPTIIs pronounced "spitties"), and everything else under the sun. The use of acronyms is so prevalent that it is like learning a new language.

I have read that it takes about three to six months to learn a job, and something happened recently, six months into the job, to prove to me I have what it takes to be the medical director. Our regional account manager (RAM) lined me up to give a presentation to our local society of oncologists/hematologists. I was apprehensive about it because oncologists/hematologists tend to be the most merciless clinicians in medicine. I think the reason for this is that they have to become hard, or they could not last in the field. They treat patient after patient who is in the same condition as Lynn Hawthorne—hopeless. I think they use up all their compassion for their patients, with none left over for the likes of me. They are a tough crowd.

Well, I held my own and got a lot of compliments about my presentation and the way I handled myself. It was like jumping over a last hurdle.

I did get a note from Lowell today, about a meeting he had with Dr. Mary Bishop, Ms. Hawthorne's gynecologist, who finally diagnosed her cervical cancer when she did a pelvic exam on Ms. Hawthorne and saw the cancerous mass and biopsied it. Dr. Bishop related to Lowell that she was surprised that she and Dr. Ken Emry (Lynn Hawthorne's family doctor) were not named in the lawsuit.

Yeah, me too.

Dr. Bishop assumes that it is only her good relationship with the plaintiff that saved the day for her, because she regards Ms. Hawthorne as not only a patient, but a friend.

How nice for her.

Dr. Bishop thinks that the physician assistant of Dr. Emry is the only one with "real exposure" in this whole mess.

Yeah, I would agree with that. The physician assistant (PA) in a fair and just world would be defending this lawsuit, because, for a period of six months after the Pap smears we saw, Ms. Hawthorne had symptom after symptom and she couldn't get in to see her doctors. Instead, several times during those six months she saw Dr. Emry's PA, who ordered lab test after lab test, X-ray after X-ray—neglecting to do what would have helped, a competent physical examination, including a pelvic exam. Over the whole time she was following the patient by herself, the physician assistant never saw a cervical mass, even during a patient visit only eight days before Dr. Bishop saw a cervical mass one and a half millimeters in diameter on the patient's cervix, from which Dr. Bishop got a tissue biopsy, which she sent to Pathology Services laboratory, where we diagnosed the cancer.

The actions or lack of actions by the physician assistant, in my self-serving opinion, led to the delay in diagnosis of Ms. Hawthorne's cervical cancer, not anything we did or Pathologists' Laboratories did.

That is, if anyone contributed to her death. Dr. Bishop is obviously very sorry about what happened to Lynn Hawthorne. Ultimately though, her reservations about Dr. Emry's PA notwithstanding, she "feels as though no one did anything wrong in her case and that she is simply a victim of bad luck." To support this, Dr. Bishop told Lowell that she remembers talking to Dr. Helen Smith, Ms. Hawthorne's gynecologist/oncologist at Ivory Hospital, who "expressed real surprise at the recurrence of her cancer and the aggressive course it took."

Dr. Bishop may be a helpful witness for us. During her conversation with Lowell, she made a point of saying several times that she "did a hell of a lot of Pap smears and never had any problems with the work of Pathology Services."

Monday, October 19, Year 2

About one and a half years after filing the lawsuit, the plaintiff side finally sent us a list of their expert witnesses, the persons who will testify against us. There are eight, none of whom is from the Dallas area, and only one is from Texas, a cytotechnologist. Some are not from contiguous states, so the other side is going to have to do the same thing we are going to do about our experts from South Carolina—prove that they have some unique expertise. Only two of their experts are pathologists.

Tuesday, November 3, Year 2

Lowell phoned me at my American Red Cross office. "I know you don't want to fool with this case anymore," he said, "and wish it would go away, but I need to ask you to do something."

"I don't have a choice," I said. "Even though I don't work at Pathology Services anymore, I know I'm stuck. I can run, but I can't hide."

Lowell laughed. "I'm putting together our expert witness list, and it's a good one, but I keep hearing about a doctor in Austin, Jennifer Stein, who would be good for us. She's looked at the slides and says it would be easy to miss the abnormal cells there, and that there was no negligence. However, she has some trouble with the way you run your lab, and she wants to meet with someone who can go over your procedures and your manuals, someone who knows what's going on—someone like you."

"Sure, I can meet with her, but you have the manuals."

"There's a lot more that I don't have. Look, she's in Dallas for some kind of cytology meeting. Is there any way you could get some time off and sit down with this lady and talk to her?"

"Sure. Why don't I just meet her at Pathology Services where all the stuff is?"

"That would be great. I'll call her right away. She has some reservations about the way you paid Billy and Bruce, on a per slide basis. Also, she has pointed out that there is a problem in the way Bruce recorded how many slides he looked at the weekend he screened Lynn Hawthorne's Pap smear. Instead of recording how many he screened Saturday and how many he screened Sunday, he just lumped everything together and recorded how many Pap smears he screened the entire weekend. Doing that is at least a technical violation of the law."

"She's right about that."

"Dr. Stein also thinks it was bad that Dr. Price didn't comment on Ms. Hawthorne's previous Pap smear results when he diagnosed cancer from the cervical tissue."

"I've been telling you that was coming," I said. "Whenever I talk to Price about it, he blusters and yells, but he doesn't have any explanation for what happened. But it's out there. So far the other side hasn't taken advantage of it, but if they are any good, they will."

"She is also upset that she read in one of the depositions that one of the pathologists hadn't even met Billy or Bruce."

"Who said that!? I don't remember anyone saying that. That's not true."

"I don't remember anything like that either," said Lowell. "She must have misread some of the testimony."

"Yeah."

"Look," said Lowell. "I know you have said (and I have said) some things critical of Dr. Price, but cool it, okay?"

"Other than the fact that he didn't comment on the previous Pap smears, let alone pull them out of the files and review them, what have I said that's been critical of him?"

"Well, I guess that's it, but you know what I mean."

"The only other thing I can think of that I have said that has been critical of him is something I've said of all the pathologists—that they want to lay the blame for the case at the feet of Billy Swenson, which is not supported by the facts."

"I know."

"As you just pointed out, as Dr. Stein pointed out, it was *Bruce* who didn't document his slide counts correctly; it was *Bruce* who did a lousy job at his deposition. Billy recorded his work accurately and did great at his deposition."

"I know. Look, all I'm saying is keep your negative thoughts about Reynolds to yourself."

"Okay. By the way, whatever happened to the settlement talks?"

"Lichty just blew me off," answered Lowell.

"I thought we were pretty close."

"Evidently the million-dollar offer on their side was a onetime shot."

"But we counteroffered with enough money to provide financial security for her child."

"Sometimes attorneys get greedy and don't do what's best for their client. They must think they have a hell of a case."

"I wasn't too impressed with their expert witness list."

"Neither was I."

"What bothers me though, is that the jury will be looking for an excuse to give Ms. Hawthorne some money, and those witnesses will give them that excuse."

"Right."

"And any shortcomings of our laboratory will be blown out of proportion, giving them another excuse to give her some money."

"I agree."

"So, I guess I'd better talk to this Dr. Stein to keep those perceived shortcomings to a minimum."

"I agree."

"This lady is going to call me today?"

"Yes."

I phoned Sarah at home to tell her what was going on. "I don't think the people at Pathology Services are going to appreciate it if you just show up. You don't work there anymore."

"Before this is over, a lot of us are going to have to put up with stuff we don't like."

Still, Sarah had a point. I tried to call Reynolds Price to give him a heads-up that I would be visiting, but the call went to voicemail. I left a message for him to call me.

Reynolds never called. Neither did Dr. Stein.

CHAPTER 19

Wednesday, November 4, Year 2

This morning I was sound asleep when the alarm rang. No, wait! It wasn't the alarm, it was the telephone. Sarah picked it up. "Oh, hi," she said. "I recognize the voice." She handed the phone to me. Our Chihuahua sat on my chest. I didn't feel very professional. The clock said 7:45 a.m.

"Hello," I said.

It was Reynolds Price. "Did you get my message yesterday?" I asked.

"Yes, and I'm not believing this. I have been trying all week to find this lady, but I can't, and now I can't find Lowell either."

"I didn't talk to her either. Now I don't know what to do."

"Call Lowell. What did you think of the plaintiff's list of expert witnesses?" asked Reynolds.

"I wasn't impressed."

"Neither was I. One, the ob-gyn is in trouble for sexual harassment. That guy in St. Louis… I can't think of his name…"

I named him.

"Right. He does not do any cytopathology whatsoever. He's just a figurehead, director of the anatomic lab or something like that. The cytotech on the list, the one from our state, I know her. She's on the Laboratory Licensing Board with me, and she didn't even tell me she was going to be testifying against us. Although, in retrospect, she was quite cool to me at the last board meeting. Usually we go out for dinner after the meetings, the whole licensing board, but last time she didn't come with the rest of us. I thought she was just tired, but she probably didn't want to face me. The crazy thing is that this lawsuit hurts her whole profession, I mean, it makes cytotechs look bad."

I went to work at my Red Cross office with the great view, and then called Lowell's office. As usual he was unavailable, out of the office the entire day. Lowell's secretary didn't have a clue about how to find Dr. Stein, who was supposed to be contacting me. Finally I talked to Lowell's paralegal, who said that Dr. Stein was staying at the Adolphus Hotel and would be calling me to set up a time to meet.

"You're sure she is going to call me?" I asked.

"Yes."

"Okay, I'll wait to hear from her."

She never called.

Friday, November 6, Year 2

It's the end of the week and I still haven't heard from Dr. Stein.

We are twenty-one months into this case and still no end in sight. My, but the wheels of justice turn slowly. I don't see how in the world this case could come to trial in June. Not a single expert witness from either side has given a deposition yet, the witnesses and lawyers are busy, and scheduling times for these depositions will take time, a lot of time.

Lowell has told me that he has never lost a trial to Dale Lichty or Scott Francis. I don't think this one will go to trial.

Saturday, November 7, Year 2

I received another envelope from Lowell today. It seems like these communications always come on Saturday, when Lowell's office is closed, so I can't take any action on the letters.

The envelope contains two documents: (1) a "Confidential" memo to file and (2) a "Dear Doctors" letter.

Both say essentially the same thing and describe a November 4 conversation Lowell had with Scott Francis about the case. Referring to Francis's expert witness list and their criticisms of our laboratory, Lowell says in the letter, "I [Lowell] asked him [Francis] if the bottom line in the case was that the cancer was there to be seen and we simply didn't see it despite two opportunities and he said yes, that's it."

About the plaintiff's experts, Lowell says that "If they will stick simply to a missed diagnosis of cervical cancer on the pap (sic) smears, then we should be in decent shape on this case."

Then Lowell says, "However, if they get in to the various technical violations committed by our laboratory, then we will have a hard time getting our own experts to say that our laboratory complied with the standard of care."

This really hurts. Granted, our laboratory is not perfect. But through the years I challenge any lab to have as good a record as ours, in any respect, including inspections and accreditation. Yet my perception is that *our attorney* never seems to miss a chance to bad-mouth our lab.

But getting beyond that, and stopping my whining, Lowell is probably just being realistic and forthright, a good thing. He evidently has observed, and been informed by our expert witnesses, that there are weaknesses in our laboratory—"technical violations."

It is not only these objective facts that bother me about Lowell's attitude, it is less tangible things as well—tone of voice, facial gestures, subtext of conversations… It is a different attitude than any attorney I have ever had about anything.

Lowell doesn't believe in us.

Wednesday, November 25, Year 2

Dr. Stein finally phoned me. This morning I was in my office at ARC when Lowell phoned me to tell me that, yet again, Dr. Stein was going to call me to set up a time to meet.

She actually, finally, did call me today, at 4:30 p.m., today, the day before Thanksgiving.

"Can we meet Friday?" Dr. Stein asked.

"Sure."

"Sorry about the time," she said. "I know the Friday after Thanksgiving is not a good day."

"When you get sued, you don't have much choice of times."

"We can reschedule."

"Friday would be fine."

"You will be in town anyway."

"Friday would be fine."

We set 10 a.m. as a good time to meet at Pathology Services lab. I gave her directions to the place. Then I called Carolyn Herring, Pathology Services' cytoprep technician, and asked her to meet me at 9 a.m. so I would be ready for Dr. Stein when she showed up. I haven't worked there for over a year, and I will have to refresh my memory about things, and I will need Carolyn's help to find what I need.

Thursday, November 26, Thanksgiving Day, Year 2

I spent much of the day going over lab records, getting ready for my meeting with Dr. Jennifer Stein.

Friday, November 27, Year 2

I arrived at the lab at 9 a.m. to meet with Carolyn and go over the pertinent on-site documents.

Carolyn wasn't there.

Kristy Bond, who I had not met, was there, and she introduced herself as the new cytotechnologist. She was tall with dark hair, slim, and looked like a model. She said, "Carolyn had to be a courier today, so she asked me to go over this stuff with you."

"We have a ten-million-dollar lawsuit looking us in the face," I said, "and I'm the only one here defending us, and I don't even work here anymore."

Kristy said, "If we'd had more notice, we could have made different arrangements."

"You found out the same time I did."

"What can I do to help?"

I told her what I needed. Kristy did not know what I was talking about. "I've only been here a few days," she said.

I phoned Suburban Hospital, where Larry Roundtree was supposed to be working, to tell him I needed help. He was the only pathologist working on this semi holiday, the day after Thanksgiving. He wasn't there. No one knew where he was, or when he would show up.

I was on my own.

We have a nice-sized lab, with plenty of space to prepare the slides and look at the slides through our microscopes. Our facilities are and always have been top notch, with the best equipment, offices, furniture, computers, and plenty of room. I went by myself to the break room to take some deep breaths, calm down, regroup, and organize what records I had. The phone rang; I picked it up. It was Carolyn. "You stood me up," I said.

"I would never stand you up, Dr. Spenser."

At that time Dr. Stein walked into the break room and gave me her card. It said Jennifer Stein, M.S., SCT (ASCP), Associate Professor at University of Texas Austin Health Science Center. I don't know what the initials mean. I suspect M.S. means master of science. "SCT" I think must stand for supervisor of cytotechnology. ASCP is the accrediting agency, American Society of Clinical Pathology.

Impressive. However, I don't see anything on her card that says she is a doctor, as I have been calling her in this diary. Therefore, from now on I'll call her Professor Stein. She looks to be in her early thirties, attractive, tall, with dark hair, and an earnest honest manner. I can see why Lowell wants her to be an expert witness for us. I do too.

The meeting started out okay; Professor Stein and Kristy Bond already knew each other—they worked together in Austin for a time. However, after the initial pleasantries, it was obvious Kristy did not have a clue about the way we had done things back when we examined Ms. Hawthorne's Pap smears. Kristy quickly left the two of us alone. After about thirty minutes Carolyn showed up, thank God. On her way to the lab, she had stopped by a warehouse to get the documents I needed.

Professor Stein had a list of questions, which I answered as best I could, but we quickly got bogged down. I said, "Why don't I just talk, and walk you through these two Pap smears from start to finish?"

She nodded yes.

It took three hours. I showed Professor Stein everything: the request slips, how we logged in the slides and patients, the worksheets the cytotechnologists used, the worksheets the pathologists used, the way Carolyn keyed in the appropriate codes in the computer, how the reports were generated, and how the reports were delivered to the clinicians. I showed her the logbooks we kept for Billy and Bruce to make sure they did not exceed the hundred-slide limit. The logbooks demonstrated the times they worked at Pathology Services and the slides they looked at. I showed how the logbook also covered the other places they worked on the applicable days, again including hours worked and the number of slides they looked at, to insure that they didn't exceed the legally mandated hundred-slides-a-day limit.

Professor Stein paid close attention and asked good questions. "I've read all the depositions," she said, "and I noticed some defensiveness about whether the cytotechnologists were independent contractors or employees. What was that all about?"

"Lawsuits are very divisive," I said. "They obviously pit patient against doctor, but they also pit cytotechnologist against pathologist, and physician against physician, because no one wants to step up and take responsibility and liability for the bad result. In every lawsuit I know about, everyone points the finger at everyone else."

"But you do recognize that you are responsible for their actions?"

"Yes."

"Who was their supervisor?"

"I guess I was, but during this lawsuit, I have backed away from it. I was terrified that my partners would point their fingers at me and say I was responsible for everything, including anything that went wrong." I pointed to the paper pile of manuals, documents, and records. "I was afraid they would say it was me who dropped the ball and didn't get things done."

"But you didn't drop the ball! You did get things done. I wouldn't back away a bit. You did a good job. You ran a good lab."

As we finished up, Professor Stein mentioned some concerns about the lab she still had. The first two we already knew about, ones that Lowell and I had discussed many times:

1. The way Bruce had lumped his weekend workloads together.

2. The lack of Pap smear/tissue correlation and Pap smear review by Dr. Reynolds Price.

Professor Stein also had four additional concerns, which I think are minor and even subjective:

1. We were doing statistical records monthly but not annually.

2. She felt our definition of a "high risk" patient, one whose Pap smear needed screening by a pathologist as well as a cytotechnologist, was not as broad as it should be.

3. She was not satisfied with our documentation of adequacy of the Pap smear specimens.

4. We were not holding reports until the 10% random rescreening by a pathologist was done. If there were problems, and the pathologist did not agree with the screening by the cytotechnologist, we were catching the reports before they reached the clinician or sending corrected/addendum reports with the change.

I don't think these four criticisms were totally valid, because industry standards of such things as how exactly to record statistics, definition of high risk, documentation of high-risk patients, and how to do 10% random rescreening are subjective.

Interestingly, Professor Stein was not bothered a bit that we paid our cytotechnologists on a per slide basis rather than by the hour. She said, "I have no doubts that your two cytotechnologists were good cytotechnologists. Lawsuits like this don't do anyone any good. Granted there are some labs that are bad, which should be shut down. But you have a good lab and this kind of lawsuit does no one any good."

Saturday, November 28, Year 2

This lawsuit is not going to do Lynn Hawthorne any good, because she's dead. Sarah woke me up this morning. "Jack!" she said. "Look what's in the paper. Lynn Hawthorne is dead!"

The Dallas Morning News obits said "Lynn Hawthorne, 37, of Iowa City, Iowa, formerly of Dallas, Texas, a radiology technician, died yesterday at University of Iowa Medical Center, cause not disclosed. Services 2 p.m. Monday. Survivors: daughter Tara Hawthorne; parents… brothers… sisters…"

Lynn Hawthorne's daughter is nine years old. The organ, cervix and uterus, that sustained her life for nine months till birth, and from which she was delivered, caused Ms. Hawthorne's death about nine years later. The tumor grew about as fast as she did.

Monday, November 30, Year 2

I phoned Lowell first thing this morning from my ARC office. I had many things to discuss.

Lowell had yet to hear from Professor Stein, and he really wanted to know how our meeting on Friday had gone. I told Lowell the two of us had hit it off, and that she seemed reasonably impressed with the way we did things. I also reported her concerns. I rambled on and on, so finally Lowell said, "Bottom line this for me."

"She's on board."

"Good. Because the last time I talked to her, which was before you got together with her, she was ready to back out."

"I can see why you want her on our side. She is personable, articulate, and obviously very conscientious."

"I agree."

"Lynn Hawthorne is dead. Did you know that?"

"I did *not* know that," said Lowell. "How do you know she's dead?"

"It was in the obits of the Saturday paper."

"Do you have a copy?"

"Not with me, but I cut the article out and put it in my files. Do you want me to fax you a copy or mail you a copy?"

"Both."

"Will do. She died without knowing that her daughter would be taken care of," I said.

"She died without knowing that her daughter would be taken care of," Lowell repeated. "Just shows you how greed by attorneys can get in the way of taking good care of the client."

"I'm so glad you said that. There may be hope for you yet."

"You think there is," said Lowell, laughing.

"Yes, to my mind five hundred thousand dollars, or seven hundred fifty thousand dollars, or a million dollars, or two million dollars—whatever it took to settle the case earlier—would be worth more to her before she died, than the entire ten million dollars that the lawsuit asks for, after she's dead. I mean, if she was alive, she could allocate it, control it, do whatever it takes to make sure it goes to her daughter. Now that she's dead, she can't do anything about it."

"This case should have been settled a year ago, if her attorneys had been on the ball."

Later, around 5 p.m., Lowell called me at my ARC office. He had talked to Jennifer Stein, who had some more information she wants me to find. She wants to know more about the log sheets for Bruce and Billy, as well as their certification. I told Lowell I would get Professor Stein what she needs.

"One final thing," Lowell said.

"Yes."

"Can you send me some diagrams or drawings or something to bring me up to speed on the staging of cervical cancer?"

"Sure."

"From experience, I know that when I depose expert witnesses, when they get backed into a corner, they start throwing all these technical terms at me, and it's easy to get buried."

"I can find some stuff for you."

"Thanks, Jack."

"Thank *you*."

Friday, December 4, Year 2

It has not been easy to find the diagrams Lowell wants. I can't find what I need in any of my pathology textbooks. There are descriptions, pictures, tables, and graphs—but no diagrams. Yesterday I phoned Bill Manley, an ob-gyn friend of mine, to see if he could help. We played telephone tag for a while, and when we finally talked, he did not know if he could help me or not. Finally, late today, he phoned me at home and said he found what I needed. I will pick up the diagrams on Monday.

Monday, December 7, Year 2

I was too busy at ARC today to stop by Dr. Manley's office to get the diagrams.

Reynolds Price phoned and we discussed my meeting with Jennifer Stein. He said there was another reason it was important that the meeting had gone well. Dr. Gable, one of our expert witnesses, was ready to bail on us. Dr. Gable told Lowell that we have a "shitty lab" and that what has happened to us is "kind of the reverse about what usually happens— usually a good lab makes a mistake and gets sued; this time there's a shitty lab that didn't make a mistake."

"Ouch," I said.

"But this is why we want to keep Lowell as our attorney. He goes the extra mile. He has Stein lined up to talk to Gable, now that you have convinced her that we have a good lab, and get him back on board."

Then a bombshell: Dr. Helen Smith, renowned big-shot gynecologist/oncologist at Ivory Medical Center, who performed Lynn Hawthorne's initial operations, apparently removed *the wrong tumor.*

This plausible scenario has been put forth by one of our expert witnesses, an oncologist. He has directed our attention to a rather confusing operation that happened after the initial operation removing the cervical cancer. This follow-up operation describes a large tumor in the vulvar/vaginal region as a "recurrence" of the cervical cancer. But he doesn't think it is a recurrence of the cervical cancer. He thinks it is a separate cancer of the vulva/vagina, unrelated to the cervical cancer, because the vulva/vagina cancer is larger and microscopically looks more aggressive. These comments make sense to me.

Thinking it through, initially Dr. Smith removed a small cervical cancer, but she missed the larger more aggressive vulvar/vaginal cancer until it was too late. The vulvar/vaginal cancer may have been hard to see on physical examination. It would not have been detected by a Pap smear. The point is that this separate vulvar/vaginal cancer was the aggressive cancer that metastasized and killed Ms. Hawthorne, not the cervical cancer.

This scenario would explain a lot of things in Ms. Hawthorne's medical history that have not made sense, specifically why her clinical course has been so dismal. Ms. Hawthorne's cervical cancer at the time of her first operation was staged as 1b, a low stage cancer with better than a 90% five-year survival. Every medical person involved in Ms. Hawthorne's care, or in this lawsuit, has been mystified as to why she has done so poorly, why the cancer recurred so rapidly and progressed so fast. Apparently Dr. Smith at Ivory removed a small tumor in the cervix, which was not particularly aggressive, but missed a larger more aggressive tumor in the vagina/vulva region, which was neglected until it was too late. This larger more aggressive cancer in the vagina/vulva continued to grow and eventually metastasized and killed the patient. That would explain his patient's horrible subsequent series of events.

And exonerate us.

CHAPTER 20

Friday, December 11, Year 2

I was finally able to get over to Dr. Manley's office and pick up the diagram of stages of cervical cancer Lowell asked me to find. It's a simple sketch of the cervix and adjacent organs with a black blob representing the cancer. As the tumor grows, the dark blob gets bigger and bigger, involving a larger volume of tissue and extending into more and more organs. Scary.

Around 11 a.m. I phoned Lowell, and miracle of miracles, he was available. The purpose of my call was to correct a couple of errors in our draft responses to the plaintiff's interrogatories. The dates of our state inspections were off a little bit. Also, the draft said that there were 50,000 to 100,000 cells in a Pap smear. That's a low estimate, actually. An accurate range is 200,000 to 300,000 cells. I asked Lowell if he wanted me to send him a reference confirming the cell count, and he said, "Sure."

"I'm sure Francis and Lichty will shake and quake when they see our responses," I said.

"I'm not so sure of that."

"I'm joking."

Lowell laughed a little, very little.

"Seriously," I said. "It's an impressive defense. Thank you."

"You're welcome."

"All joking aside, what do you think their reaction will be when they check around and see who our expert witnesses are?"

"I think they will be very impressed."

When I got home, an envelope from Reynolds was waiting. It was Ivory's surgical pathology report, describing the tissues removed during

Lynn Hawthorne's pelvic exenteration operation, a little over a year after her first operation. We still do not have the operative note of the pelvic exenteration.

I read it, and everything started to make sense. The surgical pathology report, rendered by pathologists like me, describes a tumor of the *vulva*, an organ located a considerable distance from the cervix, an organ not sampled by a Pap smear. Then there is this incredible telling sentence: "There is more nuclear atypia and pleomorphism than that seen in the previous cervical tumor."

A different tumor! This tumor, a tumor of the vulva, is the one causing all her problems, a tumor that has nothing to do with her cervix, and a tumor not picked up by a Pap smear. There is no way to blame this result on us. It's like she had a brain tumor and blamed our totally irrelevant Pap smear results.

Interesting that this information is only coming out now, almost two years after the lawsuit was filed. There is a cover-up going on. This surgical pathology report is exactly the kind of report generated to cover up something, like a second tumor in addition to the cervix cancer, which was MISSED by Dr. Smith in the first operation. Inexcusable.

At the very least, this information should fuel some great questions for Dr. Smith at trial. For example—Question: Dr. Smith, how can you rule out with certainty the possibility that a tumor other than the cervical cancer caused Ms. Hawthorne's death, for example, the separate different cancer of the vulva unrelated to the Pap smears?

I phoned Reynolds with my exciting thoughts. I was on fire. Reynolds poured water all over me. "I've already been over all this with Lowell," he said. "He doesn't want to get into it. He doesn't want to tick Dr. Smith off, wants her on our side. I pointed out to Lowell that we wouldn't be in this fix if she hadn't pointed the finger at us, accusing us of messing up the Pap smears."

"I think Smith realized she screwed up," I said. "She removed the wrong tumor, or didn't get the entire tumor out, or whatever—so she pointed the finger at us. So did Lynn Hawthorne's other physicians, the ones she couldn't get in to see. They all started mumbling about how something must have been missed on the Pap smear."

"I agree. I found out why the other side doesn't want to settle."

"Why? That has really been bugging me."

"Lowell told me. They're waiting for a state Supreme Court opinion. It's about loss of consortium, which I always thought was about sex, but it's not, or at least not only about sex. There's a case at the Supreme Court in which a kid wants money for loss of consortium for the loss of his mother, and if he gets the go-ahead from the Supreme Court, the kid will double his money."

"The other side must be very confident of a victory, if they are so worried about how much money they are going to get."

"They are so confident of victory that Lowell has been told by Francis that he is not only going to ask the judge and jury for punitive damages, but is going to file criminal negligence charges as well, so that we go to jail. You probably know this, but Mutual Malpractice will not provide us a defense for that. We would be on our own."

Monday, December 14, Year 2

Reynolds called me at work to tell me he couldn't find a copy of Dr. Smith's operation note of Lynn Hawthorne's pelvic exenteration. He wants to know if I have a copy. I said I would look in my files when I got home.

The term "operation note" or "op note" is a bit of a misnomer. It's not a brief "note," but a complete written description of the operation the surgeon performs, including the anatomy, what the surgeon encounters, what he does, what he removes—a complete description. The removed tissue specimens are sent to the pathologist, who examines the specimen and renders a surgical pathology report. I have seen the surgical pathology report of the operation, describing a tumor of the vulva, different than the original cancer of the cervix, but I haven't seen the op note.

I still haven't. I did a complete search of my files, and I do not have a copy of the pelvic exenteration op note. I phoned Reynolds and said I didn't have it.

"I'm getting very paranoid," he said. "I called over to Lowell's office and asked them to fax it to me. They sent me everything *but* the op note."

"I sense a cover-up."

"So do I. There was even a note from the general surgeon who assisted on the operation, which said 'for additional details see Dr. Smith's op note,' but no Dr. Smith's op note anywhere. Lowell's office is still looking and will request a copy from Ivory."

"Has Lowell said anything about deposing the plaintiff's experts?"

"No, I forgot to ask. I'm still uncomfortable about showing all this info this early, like the South Carolina study agreeing with our Pap smear interpretations. As soon as the other side sees it, they are going to request the slides and do their own study. I think we should hold back till the trial."

"Leave that to Lowell. We aren't going to trick them. They aren't going to trick us. It will all be out in the open."

Tuesday, December 15, Year 2

I finally turned the cervical cancer diagrams over to Lowell's office. Lowell was in a deposition and unavailable, so I gave the diagrams to his assistant, the tall blonde woman, who is a registered nurse. She let me vent. "Twenty percent of all pathologists are defendants in Pap smear litigation," I said. "If it gets too bad, pathologists will stop doing them."

"As a woman, that concerns me."

"There certainly are concerns about access to Pap smears, which National Public Radio and others are finally reporting. I don't want to be one of the casualties."

"You already are."

CHAPTER 21

Wednesday, December 23, Year 2

I received some communications from Lowell. He thinks now would be a good time to re-explore settlement talks. Between the plaintiff and defendants, there are a total of seventeen experts to depose. Lowell sent a letter to the other side pointing out that "both sides can save an enormous amount of time, money, and effort by trying to compromise and settle this matter now instead of months from now after both sides have spent a lot of money running around the country deposing experts."

Speaking of experts, Lowell sent me the list of our nine expert witnesses. It's an impressive list.

One is Dr. Ted Gable, who is chairman of the pathology department at the University of Arkansas Medical School. He will testify on our behalf.

Another is Dr. Darlene Harvey, who is on the faculty at University of Oklahoma Medical School and is a recognized expert on Pap smears. She is very personable and articulate. She is a speaker at courses and lectures on Pap smears at medical meetings throughout the country. I took one of her courses a few years ago, and she will be a fantastic witness.

A pathologist on the faculty at Ivory will testify for us. I know her as well, and she is extremely knowledgeable and a great teacher.

Jennifer Stein has signed up and will be a great asset.

I have had my disagreements with Lowell, mainly because I don't think he believes in us, but he has put up a credible defense and assembled a great list of expert witnesses.

Dr. Benedict Harris is not on the list.

Thursday, December 24, Year 2

It's Christmas Eve, and I'm listening to "Christmas in Dixie" sung by the band Alabama. Tara Hawthorne is not having Christmas in Dixie, because she is in the Midwest, and without her mother. She is not there fixing a Christmas dinner, hanging stockings, and putting presents under a tree. I cannot process or fathom that loss. Both my parents are still alive and active. My kids still have their father and mother.

I can intellectualize it and say it is not my fault that Lynn Hawthorne is dead. I contend that we did nothing wrong with respect to the Pap smears, and it is a certainty that I did not cause her cervical cancer. The cause of cervical cancer is an infection with human papillomavirus, which usually resolves, but for some reason progressed in Lynn Hawthorne to a lethal cancer. Possible reasons are that Ms. Hawthorne's immune system was not up to the task of getting rid of this particular virus, or it was a particularly virulent strain. Medicine does not have the explanation. I think it is a cosmic issue.

Why did this bad thing happen to Ms. Hawthorne, who seems to me to have been a good person, at least as good as me? She's dead, and I'm still alive and prospering, doing better than I deserve. My kids are home for Christmas for a happy time with Christmas dinner and all the presents they want. My three sons have their mom and dad, which is more than Tara Hawthorne can say. Why me? What made me so special that I live and prosper, but Lynn Hawthorne is dead, and Tara Hawthorne does not have a mother at Christmastime? Nothing.

Why did Lynn Hawthorne die? Why do bad things happen? Why is there evil in the world? And an innocent young woman dying of cervical cancer fits my definition of evil.

I don't know. *Homo sapiens* has been asking that question since the beginning of time and will be asking that question till the end of time. Persons a lot smarter than me have written about it. I refer you to Harold Kushner's *When Bad Things Happen to Good People*, or if you want a more intellectual approach, I refer you to Paul Tillich's writings: for example, *Love Power and Justice* addresses this issue, among others.

Or I can tell you what I have learned after studying this issue for a lifetime—reading countless books, attending hundreds of theological lectures during college and after, and conversing with any wise person I can find: no one knows.

Some will say there is no God, and it is a random universe. I don't believe that. I have experienced the Numinous, evidence of God.

So if God exists, why does He not stop the evil that men do, and the evil than happens that men don't do, like cancer? I believe God can't. God may be all knowing and all powerful, but cannot stop all evil, intervene yes, but stop all evil, no. There is a dark side to the creation, just as there is a dark side to humanity. We are not in the Garden of Eden anymore, and Carl Jung is right when he talks about the duality of man, that there is good and bad in all of us. There is indeed the good, but also the bad, what Jung calls the Shadow. I certainly have a Shadow in me, as my discerning readers have noticed. Good heavens, my non-discerning readers have noticed my Shadow. I try to keep my Shadow locked up so that I can be good and do good. But my Shadow is locked up in a real nice cell with cable TV, a nice little gym, plenty of good food and so forth—because the world is a dangerous place, and every once and a while I have to let my Shadow out and consult with him for some street smarts, and I cannot have him too angry at me, because I need him to give me good advice. If nothing else, my Shadow can warn me about what the dark side is planning. I think I have to do that to survive. When I am through with the consultation, back in the cell the Shadow goes.

See, this world is a tough, tough place, and in the real world, not cinema world, Forrest Gump would not last long, in spite of what his momma said. One needs at least a little guile to survive.

In summary, bad things happen, like cancer. And bad people do bad things. And I do not know why. My considered thought after a lifetime search for answers is that no one does. Reason fails me in this regard, and those who reason better than I cannot explain this mystery in ways that make sense to me.

So I have to leave reason and turn to belief, which is that God exists, and God cares. However, even God cannot stop all bad things, like cancer, death, and the bad things that men do, like assault and murder, whether it's because He is not all powerful at all times, or because we humans have free will, or something else. What is as true as anything I know is that God cares and feels our pain, and since there is so much evil in this world, what pain He feels must be… infinite.

Finally there is this: at Christmas Eve service tonight I will hear "For God so loved the world that he gave his only begotten son that whosoever believes in Him shall not perish but have everlasting life."

CHAPTER 22

Friday, January 15, Year 2

I received more letters from Lowell today. Lowell has had an extensive discussion with Dale Lichty, the plaintiff's attorney, about the lawsuit. Because Lynn Hawthorne is deceased, the remaining plaintiff is her daughter, Tara. Therefore, Mr. Lichty told Lowell that he would soon file a motion to have a guardian ad litem appointed to represent the interests of Tara.

When the talks turned to settlement, Lowell tried to get Mr. Lichty to come off the million-dollar demand, pointing out that although Tara would have enormous sympathy, the evidence is that there was no negligence or carelessness on the part of Pathology Services. Lowell did concede that "this is a clear case of an error in judgment at the very most by one or more of the cytotechs."

I am probably too sensitive. Me? Ha ha ha, but this comment came from our attorney. The results of the South Carolina study in which a majority agreed with our cytotechs and our list of experts who say the Pap smears were interpreted correctly indicate to me that this is NOT "a clear-cut case of an error in judgment" by our cytotechs.

Saturday, January 16, Year 2

Reynolds phoned me this morning. I was asleep when he called. "I read the letter you told me about," he said, "and I'm so angry that Lowell didn't bother to get our side of this stuff."

"Yeah," I said, mostly asleep.

"I wonder if we should get a new lawyer, but I guess it's a little late in the game for that."

"Yeah."

"I didn't tell you this, but I talked to Darlene Harvey. You remember who she is?"

"One of our expert witnesses." I finally started to wake up.

"Yes. She told me about a case in Oklahoma that was very similar to ours, that the defendant won."

"Yeah." Still kind of asleep.

"She told Lowell about it, and he wasn't even interested. Also I talked to Manford Johnson [the expert who conducted the South Carolina blind study that exonerates our cytotechnologists] and our case is a mission to him, to preserve the profession. He knows a lot about the expert witnesses on the other side that will make them look very bad."

"Which reminds me," I said as I finally woke up, "in the letter to Mutual Malpractice, Lowell says something that isn't true—'Please recall that each of the expert witnesses whom I have retained has criticized the laboratory's payment on a per slide basis.' That is a flat-out lie. For example, Jennifer Stein did *not* criticize how we paid our cytotechs."

"Neither did Darlene Harvey."

"I continue to be surprised that Lowell doesn't defend us more. He seems to go out of his way to come down hard on us."

"True."

"On the other hand, Lowell has done a good job of getting expert witnesses for us."

"True. But I am going to call Lowell. We have to fight this."

"Reynolds, in this chess game we don't have the status of a pawn."

Monday, January 19, Year 2

Reynolds phoned me at 11:15 this morning. I was at my office at the blood center.

"Well," he said, "Lowell took it personally. He wants to know if we want another lawyer. He said I should talk to Milton Jackson over at Mutual Malpractice myself, which I plan to do. We have to fight this. If we cave now, we will have to cave in the future."

Wednesday, January 27, Year 2

Today I received a letter from Lowell about a state Supreme Court opinion filed on January 25. Interesting that Lowell is telling me this so soon, two days later, and he sent the entire opinion. It's full of legal jargon, but the gist of the opinion is that a minor plaintiff can recover damages for loss of consortium, and this Dale Lichty will certainly try to do.

Thursday, January 28, Year 2

Lowell sent me a letter saying Lichty, the plaintiff's attorney, is "suspending" the plaintiff's offer to settle the case.

Wednesday, February 10, Year 2

Reynolds phoned me this afternoon at my ARC office.

"I bet you think I only call with bad news," he said.

"What's going on?"

"It looks like the case is close to being settled."

"That's good news, not bad news."

"Right. There are still some hurdles, some stuff to be worked out, but Lowell is working on it right now, and it looks like it's going to be settled. You'll get a letter."

"Great."

"I'll believe it when I see it."

"You've finally learned the first rule of lawsuits: nobody knows anything."

I called Sarah and told her the news.

"I'll believe it when I see it," she said.

"That's what Reynolds said."

When I got home, Sarah and Eric, my twenty-two-year-old son, were both upstairs. "Did you tell Eric the big news?" I asked Sarah.

"Nobody told me any news," said Eric.

"It's not big news till it happens," said Sarah.

Thursday, February 11, Year 2

I received a note from Lowell saying that the lawsuit was settled, and he included copies of letters to all of our expert witnesses thanking them for their help. Using this contact information, I wrote personal notes to each of our expert witnesses myself. I thanked each of them for their courage. It takes a lot of guts to stick your hand up to help in a legal case, where it can get chopped off, and that's what I told them.

The proposal Lowell made, and Lichty accepted, costs $925,000.00. And just like that, it's over.

Saturday, March 13, Year 3

Today Lowell sent me a copy of a letter from Ellen White, the attorney assigned to be the guardian ad litem for Tara Hawthorne. The letter from Ms. White is addressed to both Lowell and Scott Francis. In part it says: "As you know from our conversations, there are individuals in Iowa who were close to Ms. Hawthorne, including the personal representatives of her estate, the attorneys who drafted her last will and testament, which in part created a testamentary trust for Tara Hawthorne's benefit, and the trust officer who are <u>extremely</u> concerned about and interested in how the settlement at issue is structured and disbursed."

Ms. Hawthorne's sister and brother-in-law, parents, and ex-husband are all fighting for custody of Tara.

Although the up-front cost to Mutual Malpractice is $925,000.00, since it will be paid over time, the benefits will have a higher nominal value. The guardian ad litem's report says: "The structured settlement proposed by the Defendants has guaranteed benefits of $2,871,515.64 with expected benefits of $3,309,920.02."

Saturday, July 24, Year 3

I received a letter from Lowell saying that Judge Hand gave his approval to the settlement of the case. The details are as follows:

$350,000.00 to the law firm of Lichty, Francis and Associates.

$3,250.00 to the attorney serving as guardian ad litem.

$575,000.00 up-front cash portion, which will be used for an annuity for Tara Hawthorne providing the following:

$25,000.00 paid annually beginning at age 18 and continuing for 5 years.

$1,800.00 per month beginning at age 18 and continuing for 5 years.

$20,000.00 payable at age 21.

$50,000.00 payable at age 25.

$100,000.00 payable at age 30.

$150,000.00 payable at age 35.

$200,000.00 payable at age 40.

$2,835.00 per month beginning at age 40, guaranteed 30 years, increasing at 3% compounded annually.

Thursday, July 6, Year 4

Milton Jackson sent this letter to me and all of the defendants:

"Dear Doctors:

Your attorney has informed us that all aspects of the case Hawthorne vs Pathology Services et al have been successfully concluded. We are now closing our file.

I take this opportunity to thank you for your cooperation and assistance in our handling of this matter. If you have any questions about this file, or if we can be of service to you in any other way, please feel free to call at any time.

Sincerely,

Milton Jackson, Assistant Vice President, Claims"

I've never met Milton Jackson in person, only talked to him on the phone, but he is a class act.

The lawsuit is finally over, about three and a half years after it started.

My first rule of lawsuits remains: nobody knows anything.

So much I'll never know.

1. How would this case have turned out if it went to trial? Probably bad for us. Since the settlement of our case, a pathology group in a nearby community decided to fight a Pap smear lawsuit, and the jury found for the plaintiff for $5.5 million. Lowell was not the attorney for the defense in that case. However, Everton Hawkins, the attorney for Billy Swenson and Bruce Palmore, was the defense attorney for the pathology group, with a disastrous result. According to the local paper: "It is the largest damage award ever to come from the county courts." And the plaintiff in that case survived after "surgery, chemotherapy, and radiation therapy, which successfully attacked the tumor." Everton Hawkins may not be getting many more assignments from Malpractice Mutual.

2. Why did the cancer grow so fast, and why did nothing anyone did help this unfortunate woman? Maybe it was because Dr. Smith and Ivory Hospital were treating the wrong cancer. Let's go to question 3.

3. What happened to the op note for the pelvic exenteration done at Ivory Hospital? It was never produced by Dr. Smith or Ivory Hospital. Only by a careful reading of the surgical pathology report were we able to discover that there was a second cancer of the vulva, which looked like the aggressive cancer, which probably caused Ms. Hawthorne's problems and death—which was completely unrelated to our allegedly misdiagnosed Pap smear. To me it is obvious that there was a cover-up by Dr. Smith, who went out of her way to make sure it was difficult to discern that there was another cancer, which would have very much aided our defense, if not gotten us off the hook. Two possible explanations: (A) Dr. Smith messed up, and at the time of the first operation, a hysterectomy, she just flat out missed the vulvar cancer and did not treat it until it was too late. She did not want to be sued and blamed for a bad result, so this was a secret she kept from Ms. Hawthorne and everyone else. (B) Dr. Smith did not mess up, but knew that dissemination of this medical information would aid our defense, complicating Ms. Hawthorne's attempts to win her case and get the financial resources she needed. Dr. Smith

certainly was on the plaintiff's side more than our side, so to aid the plaintiff's case, she did everything she could to hide the evidence of a second cancer. Some candor on Dr. Smith's part would have been the honest thing to do.

Maybe it is an exaggeration to say nobody knows anything. I do know that Lynn Hawthorne is dead. The medical profession failed her. So did the legal profession. I have detailed how much time and energy I spent on our defense. On the other side, I am sure Ms. Hawthorne spent just as much time and energy fighting us. She spent the last year and a half of her life giving depositions, meeting with her attorneys, and running down medical records so she could win her case. She also had to find tax returns, rent agreements, budgets and other financial records to document what funds she needed, assuming she won the case. These were external matters that I am sure took an inordinate amount of time, time that would have been better spent on internal matters—her daughter and family, her friends, and her faith. For all her legal efforts, she died not having received a dime, the outcome still unknown.

Billy Swenson is still in the Air Force. Bruce Palmore has left the Air Force and is a cytotechnologist in a nearby community. I know the pathologist who employs him, a good doctor, who says, "Bruce is the best cytotechnologist I have ever known."

During the lawsuit, Tara Hawthorne moved with her mother from Texas to the Midwest. Then her mother died. She will grow up as a Midwesterner, not a Texan. She will have enough money to do whatever she wants to with her life. But she will have few memories of her mom.

Monday, May 28, Year 4

I am looking at slides again, at Plano Hospital, a little North of Dallas. At a local venue, I was recently one of the presenters for a College of American Pathologist course on how to do inspections, and the pathologist at Plano asked if I could help him out. He is by himself, and he wants a pathologist to cover Mondays for him so he can have a day off. He also wants me to cover his practice when he goes on vacation. I checked with my employers at the American Red Cross, and they said it was okay.

I now have two jobs.

Sarah and I are getting a divorce. I will not tell that story, now or ever. That story has been told by others. Many writers have described the loss and heartbreak of a divorce, and the gain. I will stick to *Diary of a Lawsuit.*

Monday, March 4, Year 5

Reynolds called me. "I hear you're looking at slides again. You want to look at slides for us?"

"Sure."

I now have three jobs: (1) full-time job at ARC, (2) part-time job at Plano Hospital, and (3) part-time job at Pathology Services.

I've also been promoted to State Commissioner for the College of American Pathologists Inspection and Accreditation Program. I make assignments for the CAP inspections of labs in Texas, deciding which institution is responsible for inspection of which lab. I also end up doing a lot of inspections myself here in Texas, or in other states if they need help. I travel a lot.

Monday, May 3, Year 7

I have a full-time job at Pathology Services as a staff pathologist. Reynolds and Larry are still the owners. Two other pathologists and I will buy the practice in a little over a year. I like the money, sure, but I want the chance to make Pathology Services better, the kind of place that is known for quality and excellence, a place good people want to work.

Thursday August 25, Year 8

I am one of the owners of Pathology Services. I have two partners and we have bought out Larry and Reynolds, who are retiring. We still have the same three hospitals. We have thirty employees.

The Prodigal Son has returned. I'm back to where I started when the lawsuit was filed.

I still work part time at the American Red Cross Blood Services as a medical officer. I will end my work at Plano Hospital.

Wednesday, July 20, Year 19

Today I bought out my last partner, who is retiring, and I became sole owner of Pathology Services. Call me Shogun if you wish. We still cover three hospitals and now also provide pathology services to dozens of doctors' offices, a few surgery centers, and a couple of gastrointestinal endoscopy facilities. We are a lab where people want to work, and often I have to turn down offers from other entities to buy us.

I haven't talked to or heard from Dr. Larry Roundtree since we bought him out twelve years ago. That's not new though. Even when we worked together, and were sued together, we didn't talk much. When he retired, he did not seem to be in good health because his hands shook a lot. I hear mixed reports about him. Some say he is doing well; some say he is not doing well, with neurologic Parkinson's disease–like symptoms.

Dr. Reynolds Price loves retirement. I talk to him by phone a couple of times a week. He sends me several e-mails every day with things that catch his fancy. When he retired and we bought him out, I knew I would need his advice and counsel, and I asked him to please take my calls. He said he would, and he has. The man is a political genius and a good friend.

Dr. Mary Bishop retired a few months ago. Until then she sent her Pap smears to our lab, and she was my wife's gynecologist.

Dr. Ken Emry is still practicing family medicine. We use his practice for our employee health—giving hepatitis B vaccinations and such.

Dr. Benedict Harris is deceased. He died of a glioblastoma multiforme, a malignant brain tumor, two years ago. He was seventy-four years old and retired.

I recently ran into Ms. Arnold, who is still a cytotechnologist at Christian Hospital. In fact, she now is the cytotechnologist supervisor. When I was the state commissioner of Texas for the College of American Pathologists, I made sure I never inspected her lab. I resigned as state commissioner a few years ago because I didn't have the time to do the job. Wouldn't you know it, I was assigned by the new state commissioner to inspect Ms. Arnold's laboratory. I could have turned it down, and maybe I should have, but I didn't. Interestingly Christian Hospital laboratory could have refused to let me do the inspection, but chose not to do so. I guess Ms. Arnold was okay with our "terrible" lab with a "bad reputation" doing the inspection. Or if she brought up her objections, she was overruled or, hopefully, laughed at. I believe in karma, that the good and bad you do in this life comes back in this life or the next. When she found out I was to be one of the inspectors, I suspect she put in a lot of time making sure that every little thing was in order, and had at least some stress, because if anyone was going to do an excessively thorough inspection, it would be an inspector she slandered. I was tempted to do so, but I am better than that, or too lazy. I delegated the Pap smear part of the inspection to our cytotechnology supervisor, who is personable, brilliant, and outstanding and didn't say a word about the history between Ms. Arnold and me. I handled the rest of the inspection. The inspection day passed without incident. I could hope that karma sent or will send her a $10 million lawsuit about a Pap smear she messed up—but that would be wrong.

Dr. Helen Smith, my former teacher, the gynecologist/oncologist who made sure we got sued, and then didn't want to be involved, maybe because she operated for the wrong tumor, is dead. She died unexpectedly in her sleep. She was seventy-five years old, still working at the time of her death.

Tim Anderson, my writing mentor, is deceased, which hurts a lot. I really wish he could have helped me write this book. He died of lung cancer, probably from years of smoking. A sad irony is that he quit smoking a year or so before his lung cancer showed up. He was treated at Christian Hospital, and I saw him virtually every day the last few weeks before he died. He faced his death with courage and dignity and was more worried about how his death would affect his friends and family than he was about himself.

Dr. John Pelton left Pathology Services a few months after I came back to the group. He perceived himself to be badly treated because he was never promoted to a partner/owner. He left us to work in Dallas for a competitor, but after a few months they parted ways. He then worked in Chattanooga, Tennessee, for a very large pathology group with operations throughout the state. That didn't work out either. Dr. Will Barnes, the most prominent surgeon in Chattanooga, and one of the most prominent members of the Chattanooga community, phoned down to the lab to request the help of Dr. Pelton. Specifically, Dr. Barnes had removed a segment of colon and he wanted Dr. Pelton to come to the operating room and cut open the colon for him, in the operating room, to make sure the colon lesion, in fact, was in the specimen, that it was safe to close up—a reasonable request. Dr. Pelton refused, saying, "I didn't go to medical school for four years and do four years of pathology training to be someone's boy."

End of Chattanooga.

Dr. Pelton moved around some more, finally moving to Amarillo, Texas, where he has been practicing pathology for about ten years. Recently he was arrested for child pornography. As a result, his medical license has been suspended.

Dale Lichty and Scott Francis are still suing medical miscreants. Lichty and his wife recently chaired the Steeplechase Ball, the most prestigious gala in Dallas, attended by local and national celebrities. I've never been invited. Scott Francis did finally become a judge, at least part time, two mornings a month, at a local city court. I think their firm did a credible job representing Lynn Hawthorne. I am disappointed that the settlement did not happen while Lynn Hawthorne was still alive, and I am judgmental about that. Maybe too judgmental. I am not a patient man, and the lawsuit dragged on too long in my opinion. However, from their point of view, I can see how a slow deliberate pace was in order, with no mistakes. I'm sure they were busy. They can't settle or try all their cases at once. I'm sure they did the best they could, and got what I regard as a reasonable settlement from the plaintiff's perspective.

There was quite a battle for custody of Tara Hawthorne. Lynn Hawthorne's last will and testament nominated Ms. Hawthorne's sister and brother-in-law to be guardians. There were about forty hearings, mediations, and other court events addressing the issue of who should be the guardians for Tara. The contesting candidates to be guardians were Lynn Hawthorne's parents, Lynn Hawthorne's sister and brother-in-law, and her ex-husband. Eventually Lynn Hawthorne's parents ended up with custody of Tara Hawthorne and adopted her. She grew up in Iowa City, Iowa. She graduated from Iowa City North, a public school. When Tara Hawthorne reached adulthood, she moved to a warmer place—South Beach, Miami, Florida. She rents an apartment. She does not own a house. She does not have a job. She does not own a car, preferring to ride a bike. She is not married and has no children.

Over the last several years Lowell and I crossed paths from time to time. I was sued a few years ago, for allegedly misinterpreting a bronchial washing cytology specimen, signing it out as negative, and the patient went on to develop incurable lung cancer. The plaintiff sued me for allegedly missing malignant cells. If this sounds similar to the Pap smear Lynn Hawthorne case, it's because it is. The plaintiff sued everyone who took care of him—the radiologist, the pulmonologist, the family practitioner, and me. I tried to get Lowell assigned to my defense. Why? Well, in spite of his apparent reservations about me and our lab regarding the Lynn Hawthorne lawsuit, I thought he did well to get me dropped personally from the lawsuit, and he worked hard for Pathology Services, ultimately negotiating a reasonable settlement. What I am saying is that I think Lowell is good at his job.

These factors were moot, however, because Lowell was already defending one of the other doctors in the case. It didn't take long for Lowell to try to shift all the blame to me, by grabbing the slides of the specimen to show around to other pathologists, hoping I missed something and would take all the liability. My experience is that this is the typical finger pointing that goes on during malpractice litigation, with the fingers often pointed at pathologists. Thanks, Lowell.

In the bronchoscopy specimen, there were no abnormal or malignant cells to be seen, similar to, if not the same as, the Lynn Hawthorne case. The key difference was this: Lynn Hawthorne was a totally sympathetic plaintiff, and this plaintiff was a totally unsympathetic plaintiff— a seventy-five-year-old man, smoked for fifty years, an alcoholic with a poor work history. After a couple of months, the lawsuit was dropped. I suspect the other side quickly decided the case was a loser.

Two weeks ago, Lowell died of a glioblastoma multiforme, a malignant brain tumor. He was sixty-eight years old, still working and defending doctors.

As I have said, overall, I think Lowell did a good job defending us in the Lynn Hawthorne case. I give him credit for getting Pelton, Roundtree, Price, and me dismissed as defendants individually. He helped

Pathology Services mount a credible defense so that the case was eventually settled on reasonable terms.

Lowell never did believe in us, though. I think he never got past the bad things said about me and the lab by Benedict Harris and Ms. Arnold. That didn't keep him from providing a good defense for us, because I think he took pride in his work and had high standards for himself. Nor did it stop him from using me and Reynolds as expert witnesses in some of his subsequent cases. I think he thought we were a good lab, but flawed. I think he thought I was a good doctor, but flawed.

I think Lowell is right, that I'm a good doctor, but I would add, flawed. I hope I am a good person, but I am definitely flawed.

After decades of reflection, I regard the death of Lynn Hawthorne as an accident.

It was an accident that she had an HPV cervical infection that did not resolve. HPV infections affect seventy-nine million Americans, most in their late teens and early twenties. There are fourteen million new HPV infections every year. In almost everybody the HPV infection spontaneously resolves and doesn't hurt anybody. It was an accident that in Ms. Hawthorne the infection did not go away but activated oncogenes that turned normal cells into abnormal precancerous and cancerous cells, which killed her.

It was an accident that our lab did not see abnormal cells, which would have led to appropriate prompt follow-up.

It was an accident that the small cervical cancer was not picked up earlier by her clinicians, including her gynecologist, her family practitioner, and his physician assistant.

It was an accident that Ms. Hawthorne did not respond better to the operations and treatment at Ivory and the University of Iowa Medical Center, and if the tumor of the vulva was missed initially by Dr. Smith, well, I regard that as an accident too.

I know everyone involved in her care was doing the best they could to help Lynn Hawthorne, under the circumstances at the time. No one intentionally messed up. It was an accident.

CHAPTER 23

Today

This book is a *Diary of a Lawsuit*, but it is also a survival guide. How does one survive a lawsuit? The following guidance is directed to physicians, because that's what I am, and medicine is what I know. But I think these principles apply to others as well—accountants, teachers, attorneys, ministers, professional persons, business owners, business leaders, leaders of all kinds, entrepreneurs, athletes, persons who take pride in their work, and anyone who sets high standards for what he or she does.

Recognize that you are a target. The perception of most persons is that physicians are given great power and rewards, and therefore have great responsibilities. You have put your hand up to volunteer for medical school and residency and practice, and sooner or later someone will try to cut it off. That's life and it's unavoidable. And it's not limited to physicians. Read the memoirs of business leaders, and as they get more and more successful, they become more of a target. A good example is Phil Knight's memoir *Shoe Dog*. As his fledgling company gets bigger and bigger and more and more successful, it becomes a target, especially by customs, which comes up with reasoning that Knight's company owes customs enough money to put it out of business.

I can relate to that.

Phil Knight eventually survives—with the help of powerful allies, including his senators. The case is settled for an amount of money that he can survive.

We survived the lawsuit and settled for an affordable amount.

I know I'm not as big a target as Phil Knight, and Pathology Services is not Nike. But I'm big enough that I can have a bull's-eye on my back, and lawsuits aren't the only arrows. Here's another example: It's time for Rural Hospital to build a surgery center, and it needs a Certificate of

Need (CON) from the Texas CON committee. This seemingly uncontroversial effort is opposed by a group of surgeons, my friends, who oppose the hospital venture because they want to build their own surgery center. I want to stay out of it and just look at slides, but I can't. On a Friday afternoon I get a call in my office from the CEO of the hospital. Do I know a Dr. Hadley from Waco, a pathologist, who is on the CON committee? Well, it so happens I do. Well enough that if you asked him to support our CON at the meeting on Monday, he would listen? Yeah.

So I go to the CON meeting and talk to Dr. Hadley during the lunch break, and at the meeting itself I go on record as supporting the hospital position, and my fellow physicians oppose the hospital position. The hospital gets granted the CON to build a surgery center. I get the enduring wrath of my friends and surgeons who do not speak to me, and try to get no one else to speak to me, because according to their side of the story, I sold out to the hospital.

I told this anecdote to my mother, who is still alive, and I am in my sixties. She said, "That is the price you pay for being an important person. If you weren't an important person, nobody would care what you said about the surgery center."

I'm aware that Tara Hawthorne will not have a mother when she is in her sixties.

So you are a target. Why go on? Why not go John Galt and just quit?

The answer is don't let the bad things in life, and a lawsuit is a bad thing, tint the other things in your life, the good things.

I love pathology.

Last Friday I was scheduled to work at Suburban Hospital with a full morning schedule of looking at slides, making diagnoses, and dissecting specimens. Doing science. Doing medicine. What I usually do.

In the afternoon, I had to be two places at once. A bone marrow procedure was scheduled for the pathology department to do at Pinnacle Hospital, and the pathologist there that day didn't know how to do one. At Suburban there was a needle aspiration of a lung scheduled in the afternoon, and I would have to make some slides, look at them, and make a quick diagnosis. Finally, late on that Friday afternoon there was to be a radical nephrectomy done for a malignant kidney tumor, and it would be my job to examine and dissect the specimen. I would have to describe the tumor and take relevant tissue samples for further study and diagnosis. That also had to be done before I went home, because I didn't want the kidney to sit around over the weekend.

I would have to work fast.

I drove over to the Pinnacle Hospital and went to the operating room to do the bone marrow procedure. Collecting bone marrow for diagnostic purposes is like drilling for oil. I felt the geologic landmarks of the patient's right hip region. I was looking for the right posterior iliac spine, the mother lode of bone marrow. I have used the sternum, which is easier to find and closer to the skin, especially in overweight patients. But I was going to use a big needle, and the sternum is very close to important structures such as the heart and lungs. Whenever I use a needle, I can't totally rule out the possibility of poking something I shouldn't poke, which in the case of the heart and lungs would be disastrous. There are case reports of fatal punctures of the heart and lung as a complication of sternal bone marrow procedures. So, unless I had to, I didn't want to use the sternum.

I didn't have to. My patient was a slim attractive woman with light brown hair, a mother and wife, who unfortunately had multiple myeloma, a malignant tumor of plasma cells, part of the immune system. The bone marrow exam was to see how her chemotherapy was working.

To find the right posterior iliac spine, I started at the upper portion of the right superior iliac crest, the bony bulwark forming the outer border of the hip. I felt the front of the bone with my right hand and then palpated the bone as I moved my hand toward the back until I could no longer feel it. I moved my hand three finger breadths toward the midline and then down three finger breadths. There I barely felt the right posterior iliac spine—pay dirt. I marked this region with a sterile ink pen. I washed the area with solutions to make the area sterile, and put on sterile gloves, and draped the region with sterile drapes. The anesthesiologist put the patient to sleep. With lidocaine I numbed up the skin, soft tissues, and outside of the bone. Even though the patient was asleep and would feel no pain, I didn't want her to wake up feeling sore in her hip region.

I used the sharp point of the scalpel to puncture the skin and make a small wound about the size of the bone marrow needle. There would be virtually no scar. Blood filled the wound the way a blush fills the face but stopped quickly with some pressure from a couple of sponges. When the bleeding stopped, I saw soft yellow subcutaneous fat. I slowly advanced the Illinois needle into the underlying skeletal muscle until I reassuringly reached the outside of the bone, the periosteum. Like most women only in her forties, she had very hard bones. Using all my strength, I twisted the needle back and forth and slowly advanced it through the periosteum into the bone and bone marrow. The lidocaine worked. She felt nothing. However, there is no way to numb the inside of the bone. So this next part was going to hurt, even under anesthesia. I removed the inner stylet from the Illinois needle and twisted on a 20 cc syringe. I pulled on the plunger and aspirated (sucked) bone marrow into the syringe. It looked like blood. The patient groaned, but stayed asleep, and stayed still. That part lasted only a few seconds. I handed the syringe to my assistant, who triaged the specimen appropriately—some for smears, some for sections, some for specialized studies. We had plenty. I took the Illinois needle out. I replaced it with a Jamshidi (rhymes with damn shitty) needle to collect a biopsy of the bone and bone marrow. The needle has a special design, such that when I advanced it into the bone, the bone marrow stayed in the needle when I took it out. The procedure could not have gone any smoother.

Afterwards I talked to the patient and her husband and gave them the post-op instructions—keep the area dry and take it easy. They are nice people and they thanked me. Moments like that are why I became a physician.

I got back into my car and drove back to Suburban Hospital just in time to take care of the lung aspiration cytology procedure and make a diagnosis of lung cancer. I finished up late Friday evening dissecting a kidney in which there was a golden yellow malignant tumor about the size of my hand. I described it and took the appropriate sections to look at under the microscope next week. To a layman it may sound sick, but I find this stuff fascinating. I can't wait to get the slides and see what's there, what kind of tumor it is, whether it involves the lymph nodes, or anything else. As long as I feel that way, and it fascinates me, I won't quit.

When I drove home late that Friday evening, I knew that there was nobody in all of North Texas who could have done what I did that day. Nobody.

I am sure I am not the only physician who has that feeling sometimes. In fact, anyone who has found his or her calling and takes pride in the work probably has that feeling at least from time to time.

There are good things other than work. I am remarried. We go to football and basketball games with my kids and grandkids. We travel. Or we stay around here, this part of Texas. I love the plains and how far away the horizon is, like I can look in the distance forever and not feel closed in. I feel like a cowboy. My wife and I can spend a morning at the Dallas Botanical Gardens, or around our house by White Rock Lake. The wind moves the trees by the lake, the branches swaying in the wind like fans, and the leaves rippling like the water. In our garden the morning dew makes the dark orange and light yellow mums shine like yellow diamonds, and the glistening grass in our lawn looks like a sea of emeralds.

We scuba dive, often at the Cayman Islands. Eagle rays swim by with an otherworldly look, a an ethereal look, like a spaceship, floating, rising, settling on the sand, going up and down, defying gravity, because underwater there is no gravity. As they land in the sand, they throw up sand, like dust, looking for conch. Near the surface schools of small squid line up in a V, like a battleship formation, dozens in each limb, each with large glistening eyes forward and a shimmering tail in the rear. From the edge of the reef, I like to look down off the wall into the deep blue, which goes down six thousand feet. I am awed by the vastness of the ocean, space, and the universe.

I'm also awed by togetherness and humanity. I've mentioned movies throughout this diary; after all, I left medicine to be a screenwriter, if only briefly—smartest thing I ever did. Movies are magic.

The most powerful scene in any movie I have ever seen takes place in *Places in the Heart* starring Sally Field (she won an Oscar) and the scene is the last one. The movie is set in small-town Texas cotton country in the 1930s, and it is not a good time. It is Depression time, and in some ways, a depressing movie. For years I refused to watch it, because I do not like depressing movies. In film school, I had to watch it because it was an assignment. The sheriff (Sally Field plays his wife) is accidentally shot at a railroad station, by a young African American man, who in turn is brutally killed by a vigilante mob. You can see why I held off watching it. I don't like violence. The Sally Field character tries to hold on to the family farm, and some of the respected and powerful members of the community, including a banker and cotton merchant, try to cheat her and grab the farm. Again, you can see why I held off watching it.

The Sally Fields character with the help of family, a blind man, an African American man, and some miracles saves her farm, and the story moved me. But it is the last scene that brings tears to my eyes every time I see it or think about it. The setting is a small church, and it's communion, and EVERYONE in the narrative attends the service, living and deceased. They take communion in the pews, passing the wine and wafers from one person to the next. In the beginning, those who are alive pass the communion, the righteous and the unrighteous, one to another, adults to children, a white man to a black man, and a blind man to one who sees—and finally at last to the Sally Field character sitting in a pew at the back of the church, who is alive, who passes the communion to her husband, who has died but is there, who passes the communion to the deceased young African American who shot him who was savagely killed, but is present at communion, and they reconcile. The scene is reconciliation. Man, we are all in this together.

I think the scene resonates with me so much because communion resonates with me so much. We had communion at my wedding ten years ago. One of the big reasons we go to Christmas Eve service is that communion is part of the service. My favorite Sunday to attend church is the first Sunday of the month, when we have communion. I take that opportunity to pray for me, and my family, and my friends, and for my ways to be guided to do the right thing, and to not be led into temptation.

Look, I'm not trying to convert anybody here; I'm not a minister or a theologian, just a guy trying to understand life and death like everyone else. We all have to come to terms with this life and this death, and some in this story I have told are already deceased.

However.

I would like some day to have communion with Scott Francis and Dale Lichty, if not in this world, maybe the next. I have no doubt they were trying to do the best for their client within their human limits.

I would like to have communion with Ms. Arnold, who was young when she said terrible things about me, and probably thought she was doing the right thing, righting wrongs, straight out of school, when she still wanted to change the world.

I would like some day to have communion with Lowell Pound and Benedict Harris, which will have to happen in the next life. Lowell may not have believed in me as a client, but I was lucky to have him as my lawyer. Benedict Harris probably didn't realize the hurt he caused me when he believed Ms. Arnold, and was just telling the truth as he saw it.

I would someday like to have communion with Tara Hawthorne. I hope she does not blame me for the death of her mother. If she does, I can only answer her that I did the best that I could. Maybe I wasn't a smart enough pathologist, and my lab wasn't good enough, and my cytotechs weren't good enough, but all I can say is I did the best I could, *we all* did the best we could, and in this life, sometimes that just isn't enough.

I would like someday to have communion with Lynn Hawthorne. I often wonder if she blames me for her death. Around me she comported herself with such dignity, it's hard to know. She was in the medical field, an X-ray technologist, and understood the imperfections of X-ray testing, and it is not farfetched to think she understood the limits of lab testing as well, and the limits of Pap smears. I hope she was just going through the motions of blaming us so that her daughter could have the resources she would need. Did Lynn Hawthorne really think our lab was bad, and we were bad, and I was bad, or was she just saying that in a lawsuit to get what she needed for her daughter, soon to be without a mother? I'll never know. I guess it doesn't make that much difference in the grand scheme of things, but maybe it does, because I think everything one does makes a difference. Every life is important. I am not sure she ever knew the truth because she died well before many of the facts of our defense were known. Had she lived longer, she might have seen that some of our defense had merit, but that would not have changed her goal, to get the resources her daughter would need, by any means necessary, and the lawsuit was her best chance. I understand that. In her shoes I would have done exactly the same thing. So would anyone, but it's over. Someday I hope to have communion with Lynn Hawthorne.

About the Author

Dr. Spenser is a practicing physician who has written several scientific articles published in various medical journals. This is his first book.

Made in the USA
Coppell, TX
16 April 2023

15684027R00104